THE Earthpeople
ACTIVITY BOOK
People, places, pleasures & other delights

Other Goodyear Books in Science, Math, & Social Studies

THE CHALLENGE OF TEACHING SOCIAL STUDIES IN THE ELEMENTARY SCHOOL
Dorothy J. Skeel

DR. JIM'S ELEMENTARY MATH PRESCIPTIONS
James L. Overholt

ECONOMY SIZE From Barter to Business with Ideas and Activities
Carol Katzman and Joyce King

LEARNING TO THINK AND CHOOSE Decision-Making Episodes for the Middle Grades
J. Doyle Casteel

LOVING AND BEYOND Science Teaching for the Humanistic Classroom
Joe Abruscato and Jack Hassard

MAINSTREAMING SCIENCE AND MATHEMATICS Special Ideas and Activities for the Whole Class
Charles R. Coble, Paul B. Hounshell, Anne H. Adams

MATHMATTERS
Randall Souviney, Tamara Keyser, Alan Sarver

THE OTHER SIDE OF THE REPORT CARD A How-to-Do-It Program for Affective Education
Larry Chase

SELF-SCIENCE The Subject Is Me
Karen F. Stone and Harold Q. Dillehunt

THE WHOLE COSMOS CATALOG OF SCIENCE ACTIVITIES For Kids of All Ages
Joe Abruscato and Jack Hassard

This book is part of the Goodyear Series in Education, Theodore W. Hipple, University of Florida, Editor.

For information about these, or Goodyear books in Language Arts, Reading, General Methods, and Centers, write to:
Janet Jackson
Goodyear Publishing Company
1640 Fifth Street
Santa Monica, CA 90401
(213) 393-6731

THE Earthpeople
ACTIVITY BOOK
People, places, pleasures & other delights

Joe Abruscato
University of Vermont

Jack Hassard
Georgia State University

Goodyear Publishing Company, Inc.
Santa Monica, California

Acknowledgments

Many earthpeople have made this book possible. First and foremost are our parents, to whom we dedicate this book: Josephine and Nunzio Abruscato and Margaret and Russell Hassard. They have given us their love and acceptance so that we each could develop and grow in the ways that we chose.

Sandy Booth and Sue Randolph from Atlanta and Mary Lou Wasko from Burlington interpreted our writing and transformed it into a typed manuscript. These wonderful people were more than typists; they cared about what we were doing and we care deeply about each of them.

Janice Gallagher and David Grady have again provided us with the guidance and encouragement to develop and write the book. These two people, who were at our side on our two previous books, Loving and Beyond and The Whole Cosmos Catalog of Science Activities, gave us professional and personal attention, for which we are very grateful. Thank you, Janice and Dave.

And now, to you, our students. Our books have always grown from our desire to provide you with more and better ways to meet the challenges that lie ahead. The relationships that we have formed with you in the process of growing together are gifts that we will always treasure. You, in so many ways, have been our sources of encouragement and hope for the future. We love you and wish you peace and joy on your journey.

Copyright © 1978 by Goodyear Publishing Company, Inc., Santa Monica, California 90401

Current printing (last digit)
10 9 8 7 6 5 4 3 2 1

Y-2326-0 (C)
Y-2318-7 (P)

Printed in the United States of America

Designer and Art Director:
  Tom Lewis
Editorial Supervisor:
  Jackie Estrada
Cover Design by Tom Lewis
Cover Illustration by
  Ted Brentlinger

Illustrators:
Robbie Adkins
Janet Colby
Jim Dearing
Carol Kerr
Tom Lewis
Dennis Merrit
Linda Roberts
Don Young

Library of Congress Cataloging in Publication Data

Abruscato, Joe.
  The earthpeople activity book.

  (Goodyear series in education)
  Includes index.
  1. Science — Study and teaching (Elementary) — handbooks, manuals, etc. 2. Arithmetic — Study and teaching (Elementary) — Handbooks, manuals, etc.
I. Hassard, Jack, joint author. II. Title.
LB1585.A27   372.3'5'044   78-7602
ISBN 0-87620-232-6
ISBN 0-87620-231-8 pbk.

Contents

How to Use This Book

The Earthpeople Activity Book is for kids, parents, and teachers to enjoy. There are activities to do, games to play, biographies to read, challenging puzzles to work, arts and crafts projects to brighten rainy days, and other delights.

The book is organized into six sections.

1. The Amazing Earthpeople —some psychology and social and cultural anthropology

2. Earthpeople—History and Herstory—the struggle for human rights, plus heroes, heroines, and rascals

3. Beautiful Earthship—a touch of geology, geography, and ecology

4. Peopledoings Around the World—earthpeople pleasures such as sports, crafts, and music making

5. Earthpeople Tomorrow— ideas about the way we will be

6. Appendix—a few gameboards and other special things.

The contents and the index will lead you information detectives to whatever you are looking for.

There are 932 ways to use this book. Here are 16 that we have come up with.

1. Read the book from cover to cover.

2. Read the book backwards.

3. Use the flip technique. Hold the book firmly in your left hand. With your right hand flip the pages from front to back. Stop on the page that catches your eye.

4. If you are a teacher, obtain two copies. With a single-edge razor blade carefully remove the cover. Laminate the pages and use each chapter as the nucleus for a series of learning centers. The other book is in case you goof!

5. Teachers, again, select a concept in the social studies, identify activities in the book, and develop a unit on the idea.

6. Integrate activities from the book into your social studies units.

7. Divide your class into groups of three. Have each group share one activity with the whole class.

8. Choose one person featured in The Earthpeople Activity Book each week for a bulletin board display, classroom meeting, or library search.

9. Use the book backwards with your kids. They'll love it!

10. Use the book as the basis for your social studies program. Having one copy for each group of students will save you much Xeroxing.

11. Let a student open randomly to any page. That page is the social studies lesson for the day!

12. Turn the pages, enjoying only the artwork and pictures.

13. Read about all the people who are featured in the book.

14. Employ the stab process. Stab blindly at any item in the index. Using your right index finger, turn to the page number indicated.

15. Give the book to one of your friends. Think generously.

16. Write to the authors and tell them how you feel about the book. Think kindly.

Introduction

The Earthpeople Activity Book is about the people who have lived and are now living on a planet that is very tiny compared to the giant Milky Way galaxy in which it's located. The tiny planet is called earth and the people who share the planet with each other are known as the earthpeople. This book contains activities, ideas, and information about the joys, hopes, and dreams of the earthpeople. It is a book about you and a book about all of us. It is a book whose activities will help us understand where we have been, where we are today, and, perhaps, where we will be tomorrow.

One of the subjects taught in earthpeople schools is social studies. Young earthpersons spend a great deal of time learning about history, geography, economics (money), anthropology (similarities and differences between people from near and far), and many other "things." *The Earthpeople Activity Book* will help you do much more than "learn about things." It is a social studies book that is quite different from other social studies books you may have used.

This book is about *all people*. *The Earthpeople Activity Book* is about black people, white people, red people, yellow people, brown people, young people, old people, past people, present people, and even future people.

This book is about *hope*. We have confidence in the people of earth. Although we have many problems facing us in the world today—hunger, wars, poverty, pollution, and serious crime—we also have hope. We believe that every earthperson has a desire to put these rampant problems to rest. In this book we explain some ways that earthpeople have tried to solve these problems. We have hope. . . .

This book is about *courage*. Just as our heart is the pump that lets us live, so is courage the pump that lets us face dangers and difficulties. The heart primes our bodies as courage primes our souls. Courage is the driving force that directs earthpeople to stand up for their beliefs, for their dignity, and for their freedom. Within these pages we have written about some of the people whose courage has made our planet a better place to live.

We want this book to be *fun* for you. We believe in the importance of humor, the sort of humor that makes us playful. The word "fun" comes from the word "fonner" meaning "to be foolish." To be foolish is to be amusing, playful, open, and jovial. Having fun in life helps us become more free and creative, even though we realize that the discoveries we make in the process may be serious.

We hope that you enjoy using this book. We have enjoyed putting it together. It has helped us understand ourselves, our teaching, and our relationship to our brothers and sisters with whom we share this tiny planet.

Our Roots

There are many ways to explain what started the universe and humanity on their way. These explanations are called theories. One theory is that the cosmos (all things in the universe) began 10 billion years ago.

According to this theory, our sun, other stars, and planets in our solar system were formed over a period of a few billion years. Life on the planet earth probably began to develop about 3 billion years ago. Many people believe that a watery environment such as ancient shallow seas housed the first form of life. But the most startling

theory of all is that the first humans—our ancient brothers and sisters—didn't appear until about 2 million years ago.

This chapter takes you on a journey backward through time to the beginning of the universe and forward from there to the discovery of human fossils. The trip is a long one, with many mysteries along the way. You'll find that no one knows the answers to every question about the way in which we began, but have fun as you dig in and uncover some clues about your roots.

THE BIG BANG

A ONE-ACT PLAY

Suppose someone asked you, "How do you think the universe began?" What would you say or do? Here is one way to answer that question. It contains very few words but a lot of action!

Many scientists believe that the universe began with a big bang about 10 billion years ago, when all the matter in the universe was held together in a huge cosmic mass.

According to this theory, the expansion of the universe occurred when this mass exploded, sending all its matter into space. To help you understand this theory a little better, read the following play. Then gather together some of your friends and produce your own big bang.

The play has two main characters, The Great Sound in the Sky and Cosmic Mass Particles. The Great Sound in the Sky is played by a person who is good at humming and has a loud voice. Cosmic Mass Particles, played by as many people as you can get together, are fast runners as well as able hummers. The set for the play is a large empty space—a room, gymnasium, or field.

Enter *The Great Sound in the Sky* (stands near the outside of the empty space):
Hummmmmmmmmmm.

Enter *Cosmic Mass Particles* (slowly move toward the center of the empty space and gently crowd together, packing as close together as possible).

The Great Sound in the Sky (speaks to the Cosmic Mass

Particles): I am the energy source of the cosmos. You are the particles that make up the mass of the cosmos. Imagine that each of you is an original particle or atom existing at the time of the origin of the universe. Everything that is here today was here when the universe began, but in a different form. I am going to ask you to start humming. This sound is the energy we need to get the universe started. When the sound gets loud enough, you will explode by running to the outside of the empty space. Now:

Hummmmmmmmmmmmm.
Hummmmmmmmmmm.
Hummmmmmmmm.

Cosmic Mass Particles:

Hummmmmm.
Hummmmmmmmmmmmmmm.
Hummmmmmmmmm.
Hummmmm.

The Great Sound in the Sky: Louder.

Hummmmmmmmmmmmmmm.
Hummmmmmmmmmm.
Hummmmmmmmm.

Cosmic Mass Particles (hum louder):

Hummmmmmmmmmmmm.

The Great Sound in the Sky:

Hummmmmmmmmmmmmm.
Get ready to **EXPLODE!**

Cosmic Mass Particles run to the outside of the empty space.

After getting yourself back together, consider the following questions:

1. What was your reaction to playing the part of either The Great Sound in the Sky or a Cosmic Mass Particle?

2. What were some of your thoughts as the sound began getting louder?

3. How did you feel at the moment of the big bang?

4. Find some books that discuss the big-bang theory and make a list of the evidence that people use to support it.

5. Find out what other theories people have developed to explain the origin of the universe.

Thinking About

Here are several brief "biographies" that will help you learn about what some of our ancestors may have been like.

Australopithecus africanus—African ape-man

This African ape-man lived from 5 million to 750 thousand years ago. An ancestor of modern human beings, Australopithecus had a brain about the weight of that of a big ape (1½ lbs.). The development of a larger brain was probably responsible for the ape-man's first great invention—a primitive stone tool. A single blow to the edge of a stone created a tool that was useful for striking and cutting. Australopithecus had a life span of about 20 years. Thus most Australopithecus children were probably quite young when their parents died. This phenomenon probably led to a primitive form of social group in which children were taught by "adopted" parents.

1. Go outside and find a stone. Without using any additional tools, fashion the stone you found into a cutting and striking implement.

2. How are children in our culture taken care of if their parents die?

Homo erectus—Erect man

Homo erectus was a true "man," erect standing with a heavier brain (almost 3 pounds). This species of Homo spread to Europe, Asia, East Indies, and Africa. Homo erectus hunted bigger game, made better tools, and was probably the first human to use fire. The most famous fossil of Homo erectus is Peking man.

Homo erectus, because of a larger brain and changes in the hand, was able to refine the quality of the original primitive stone tools.

our Ancestors

1. The changing of humankind has proceeded at a faster rate than other animal species. What do you think are some reasons for this?

2. How do you think the tools of Homo erectus compared to the tools that the Pilgrims had available in the 1600s?

3. Inventing tools is a creative act. Collect an assortment of materials such as bottles, nails, string, wheels, screws, and hammers. How do you think these tools were invented?

Homo sapiens—Early man

Men and women who first began to look like us were preceded by Swanscombe man in England and Germany, Neanderthal man in Europe, and Rhodesian man in Africa. These earlier ancestors looked very different from us.

Let's take a close look at Neanderthal man. With a brain as large as ours today (1450 cm³), Neanderthal man survived the Ice Age by using intelligence to make flint spearpoints to kill animals for food. These early people buried their dead with tools, indicating a religious belief in some type of afterlife.

1. Cro-Magnon man lived about the same time as Neanderthal man. Find a book on early man to determine how Cro-Magnon differed from Neanderthal man.

2. How do you think Neanderthal man survived the period of time when ice began to cover much of the earth?

Homo sapiens—Modern man

Modern "man" was first a hunter and gatherer. Early men and women had to move great distances to gather food. At the present time, most scientists believe that modern man began in Africa, quickly spreading to Java, China, and Europe. We are essentially Ice Age creatures who have developed a culture during the last 100 thousand years. The most recent glacier melted away from what is now northern Ohio about 10 thousand years ago. Modern Homo sapiens stalked animals, lived in caves, created art, developed religion, and invented new tools.

1. Modern "man" was a hunter-gatherer of food. How are we alike or different now, given the rapid rise of agriculture and the industrial revolution?

2. Cave paintings are interesting and exciting relics of our roots. Why do you think individuals painted scenes of animals on the walls of caves?

ABOVEGROUND ARCHAEOLOGY

There are many artifacts that can help you understand the way things were. Many are underground, and only someone with special training should disturb them. Some artifacts that you can discover without ruining an archaeological site are those things from the past that remain above the ground.

Clues to the past go unnoticed most of the time and are not buried in the ground at all. In an attic or cellar, or in the storage room of an apartment or garage, you may discover things that were used many years ago and have been put away and forgotten. At one time they were useful or valuable in the everyday life of mothers and fathers, grandmothers and grandfathers, or those so far back in family history that they are only names dimly remembered or quite forgotten. Some intelligent information gathering with these clues may result in a picture of what it was like to live before automobiles, airplanes, motorcycles, dishwashers, electric dryers, clothes washers, television, radio, telephones, air conditioners, and electric lights. You may gain a feeling of how it was to cook without gadgets and gas or electric stoves, stitch without a sewing machine, drive a horse, or read by candlelight.

Clues to the past may also be uncovered in old letters, notes, diaries, newspapers, magazines, and in books of many kinds. An old textbook from 50 or 100 years ago or even more is excellent evidence of what and how people in school were learning at that time. An old children's book or a game or toy may tell much about familiar, everyday experiences of our ancestors. You can do much interesting research to discover how old games, including baseball, football, basketball, and hockey, were played many years ago under their original rules and field markings.

Looking into the evidence of the past does not mean disturbing what the family has stored away and then getting tired and leaving it in disarray. This is as bad as digging up an ancient site with picks and shovels and looting whatever you find, making no records of what you found and how you found it. As in archaeology, training and supervision are needed, but you can practice conserving data with some common-sense procedures.

Here is a system you can use to start recording the past way of life in your community or the activities of your own family. Set up a file of 3×5 or larger cards and type or print neatly the information needed to identify and describe the item you want to inventory and catalogue. You may wish to set up an A file for artifacts or objects and a D file for documents. At the top of the card, describe the first artifact as A-1-1978 (the date of discovery). Next, identify the object and write down where it is found. Then write a descriptive sentence or two with any pertinent data, ownership by any particular individual, for example. A sample of such a card is shown below. Your D file card for documents would be the same, substituting D for A in your descriptive code.

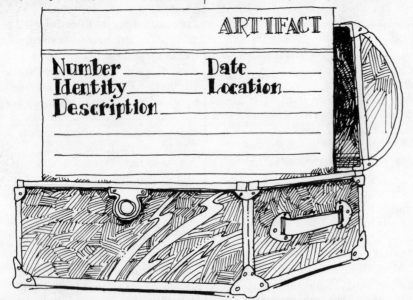

ARTIFACT

Number _____ Date _____
Identity _____ Location _____
Description _____
_____
_____

UNDERGROUND ARCHAEOLOGY

Person-made objects, or artifacts, that tell us how life was in the past are valuable. No, they usually aren't very valuable as far as money goes; they are valuable because they tell us about the way we were and, if we make some good guesses, about the way we may be.

Perhaps you've seen films of scientists uncovering artifacts. Did you notice that they are very careful to keep the objects from breaking as they clean the soil from them? Underground archaeology should really be done only by trained people so that all of us can benefit from discoveries. *Never* dig up areas that may contain artifacts just for the fun of it or just to collect artifacts.

If you are really interested in belowground archaeology, the best thing to do is to contact a group of people who are experienced archaeologists and ask to join them on a dig. Write to the U.S. government or to universities or museums for information and address lists.

Activities on this page are from the booklet "Aboveground Archaeology," available from the Superintendent of Documents, U.S. Government Printing Office, Washington, D.C.

Art From the Earth

One of the things archaeologists have learned about early cultures is that art was as important as food, clothing, and shelter. Early cultures considered themselves a part of nature and found great pleasure and beauty in it. Art from earlier cultures is sometimes called "primitive" art, but the art forms of these cultures were of a very high quality and sophistication.

The earth itself provides us with many materials for art forms. Let's use two of them—soapstone and clay—for rock carving and pottery making.

Rock Carving

Carving is an old craft that takes great skill but is also fun.

Materials

Small pieces of soapstone (soap, if you cannot get soapstone)

2 files (round and flat)

Gauge or screwdriver

Newspaper

Baby food jar

Sandpaper

Carving Out a Place for Yourself

1. Hold the soapstone in your hand and close your eyes. Take some time to become familiar with the stone. Turn it slowly in your hand, feeling for ridges and surfaces. Now open your eyes and continue observing the stone.

2. Put the soapstone on a piece of newspaper and begin to carve it with one tool. As you carve, a fine, slippery white powder will collect on the newspaper. Save this powder in the baby food jar.

3. Try each of the tools on the stone to give yourself an idea of how the different tools carve the stone.

4. Continue carving. What you carve is, of course, up to you. You might want to make a carving of an animal, a person, or something abstract.

Pottery Making—Without a Wheel and Kiln

Pottery is made from clay, which is a very fine-grained form of soil. You can create a variety of objects by molding clay in your hands.

Materials

Quick-hardening clay

Pencil or stick

Paint brushes

Large pieces of newspaper

Proceeding With Pottery

1. Roll the clay into a ball and work it around in your hands.

2. Use your fingers to mold the clay into whatever you want to make: plaque; figurine of a man, woman, child, or animal; medallion; or pendant.

3. After you have finished molding the object, let it dry for about 24 hours. If you are going to make any grooves or markings, use a sharp pencil before the clay dries.

4. Use the paints to decorate your object.

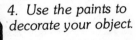

Cave Art:
PRIMITIVE GRAFFITI

Humans have been artists ever since they discovered that they could make pictures of the animals they hunted and the gods they believed in. Pictures made by early human beings appear on walls of caves and on pieces of stone. This doodling, or primitive graffiti, is how our ancestors got the idea for writing. These pictures of objects became a way to express ideas. Later humans developed very complicated languages as they began to give more meaning to pictures.

In this activity, you have an opportunity to do some creative artwork.

Materials
Drawing paper
1 roll of butcher paper
Paint brushes
Newspaper or plastic covering
Old shirts (to cover up your good clothes)
Scissors
Baby food jars

Paints (To make your own colors, collect different colors of berries, grass, and so forth, then crunch and mix with small amounts of linseed oil.)
Crayons

For Graffiti Gourmets
1. Take a field trip outside and collect as many objects as you can. Make an art form with some of the objects, paint, and paper. Try to express in your art form how you feel about the environment from which you collected the materials.

2. Line one wall of your room with butcher paper. This will be your graffiti wall. Invite other people to express their feelings and thoughts on the wall using a variety of paints, crayons, and pencils. Encourage people to draw, write, and invent their own symbols. Later, gather people together for an interpretation session: Guess at Graffiti.

3. Ask your teacher and principal to donate an unused wall either inside or outside the school for your services as an artist to help beautify the school. You might have to "canvas" for this privilege. If you get approval, create a wall that archaeologists will be excited to discover 2000 years from now.

THE TIME CAPSULE

What do you think future anthropologists and archaeologists will study to find out about the human species during the 1970s? Imagine that you are a member of a team of scientists who are compiling a list of items that have been a part of American culture for the past 10 years. These items will be sealed in a time capsule that will not be opened for 1000 years. The capsule is ½ m (about 1½ ft.) in diameter and 3 m (about 10 ft.) in length, and your team is restricted to ten items.

Time to Proceed
1. In a large group, brainstorm a list of possible items. Have one member of the group write the items on a large sheet of paper. Do not evaluate the items that are called out but use the items as ideas for new ones.

2. In small groups, select the ten items that should be placed in the time capsule. As you list each of these items, state why you think the item should be included. Your group might produce a chart similar to the one that follows.

3. When the lists are complete, each group should then construct a time capsule. Put each item into the capsule and select a safe place for burial.

Item for Time Capsule	Reason
NASA photo collage of the earth	To describe visually the earth's surface
The top-selling record album of the decade	To demonstrate our musical abilities
A video-tape replay of the last Super Bowl	To show one of our sports

Being a Cosmic Observer

Another way to find out about humans is to imagine that you are a visitor from outer space and that you are here to observe the amazing earthpeople! Here's how to go about being a cosmic observer.

The Fantasy Trip

Find a comfortable place and have someone read this fantasy trip to you.

I'd like you to close your eyes and relax. . . . Take a deep breath. . . . Now, imagine that you are from another planet in the universe. . . . What is the planet like and where is it located? . . . What are your planet's people like? . . . What do they look like? . . . What do they do? . . . You have been asked to travel to the planet earth. . . . How does this make you feel? . . . You will inhabit the body of a human when you arrive. . . . You are traveling to earth and landing on the planet. . . . What was your trip like and where did you land? . . . What is the person whose body you now inhabit like? . . . Just think about this for a few moments. . . . Now come back to the room and slowly open your eyes. . . . You are now on the earth as a cosmic observer. . . . Share your trip with others and explain why you are visiting earth, if you wish.

Observing Earthpeople

This part of the activity must be done where there are other earthpeople. Choose from the following earthpeople places: playground, amusement park, city park, busy street corner, shopping mall, or restaurant.

Take this list of questions with you while observing the amazing earthpeople.

1. What do humans like to do? Why?

2. How do humans communicate with one another?

3. How do humans feel about one another?

4. Carry on a conversation with humans. How do they react when talking to you, a stranger?

5. Are there some things you observe humans doing that you like? That you dislike?

6. How do humans treat other inhabitants of earth, animals, for example?

7. How are humans different from the inhabitants of your home planet?

8. What do humans believe in? What do they think will happen when they die?

When you have completed your observations prepare a twenty-five word telegram about earthpeople to send to your home planet.

COSMIC UNION

_____
_____
_____
_____
_____
_____
_____

signed

Some Amazing Books

Arundel, Jocelyn. *Land of the Zebra*. Ranger Rick's Best Friends Series, no. 3. Washington, D.C.: National Wildlife Federation, 1974.

—. *Lions and Tigers*. Ranger Rick's Best Friends Series, no. 3. Washington, D.C.: National Wildlife Federation, 1974.

Baldwin, Gordon C. *Inventors and Inventions of the Ancient World*. New York: Four Winds Press, 1973.

D'Aulaire, Emily, and D'Aulaire, Ola. *Chimps and Baboons*. Ranger Rick's Best Friends Series, no. 3. Washington, D.C.: National Wildlife Federation, 1974.

Goode, Ruth. *People of the Ice Age*. Illustrated by David Palladini. New York: Macmillan, Crowell-Collier, 1973.

Gray, Robert. *Elephants*. Ranger Rick's Best Friend Series, no. 3. Washington, D.C.: National Wildlife Federation, 1974.

Shapiro, Harry L. *Peking Man*. New York: Simon & Schuster, 1975.

Jane Goodall,

FRIEND TO CHIMPANZEES

One way to learn more about humans is to study the behavior of those animals that are most closely related to us, such as chimpanzees. One scientist who has spent many years studying how chimpanzees behave is Jane Goodall.

Dr. Goodall has spent most of the last 16 years following and sometimes even living with chimpanzees near Lake Tanganyika in Africa. Because the chimpanzees wander over great distances in search of food, it is very difficult to keep up with them. To make studying them easier, she built a feeding area where the chimpanzees could come for food. As a result, they would stay near the area and could more easily be observed.

© National Geographic Society

Dr. Goodall has learned many things about chimp behavior, including certain things that they seem to have in common with the amazing earthpeople: cooperation, strong attachment of the young to one another and to their parents, and problems that a chimp goes through when approaching adulthood. In recent years she has been a visiting professor at Stanford University and is the scientific director of the Gombe Stream Research Center in Tanzania, Africa. Scientists from all over the world come to this very special place on the banks of the Gombe Stream to study the behavior of the animals of the African forest.

1. Do you think that following a group of chimpanzees as they roam through a forest would be fun? Why or why not?

2. If you were observing chimpanzees, what would be some interesting things to watch for?

3. Do you think that we can learn anything about human beings by studying the ways in which animals behave?

The Baboons of Nairobi Game Park

The Nairobi Game Park is near the city of Nairobi, which is the capital of Kenya, Africa. The animals that live in the park include lions, giraffes, zebras, and baboons. They are protected, as are animals in the national parks of the United States.

Baboons are primates like us. They are also very social animals, living in groups for the purpose of survival. A baboon group is called a troop and can have a population of over 100 members.

One way to learn about ourselves and our roots is by studying animals that are similar to us. In this activity you will observe the behavior of a baboon troop through the eyes of the anthropologist Irven DeVore. You are about to read the actual field notes that he recorded while observing baboons for one day.

As you read the field notes, you will find abbreviations and symbols used to note observations. To help you understand the notes, here are some symbols that you should become familiar with.

LT = Lone Tree baboon troop
SR = Songora Ridge baboon troop
ad♂ = Adult male baboon
ad♀ = adult female baboon
s/ad = sub-adult baboon
j_2 = Older juvenile baboon
j_1 = Younger juvenile baboon
i_2 = Older infant baboon
i_1 = Younger infant baboon

Read Irven DeVore's field notes (page 10) to find out how baboons live. Find someone else who has also read the field notes and discuss how the baboon troop lives. What are some things that you both have in common with a baboon troop?

Being an Anthropologist

After reading the field notes you might enjoy making careful observations based on DeVore's field notes. To do this you should use the Observer's Card for Studying Baboons. The observer's card focuses on three of the social behaviors of baboons: play, conflict, and eating. Select one of the three behaviors and begin to read through the field notes, looking for the first example of this behavior. Answer the questions on the observer's card. Continue to read, repeating this procedure for each incident of the one behavior.

Complete the observer's card for the two other behaviors. When you are finished, see if you can answer the following questions:

1. *What did you learn about the behavior of baboons?*
2. *Do you think play is important to baboons? Why?*
3. *What do baboons fight about? How does this compare to human fighting?*
4. *How are baboon eating habits different from human eating habits?*

Adapted with permission from Man: A Course of Study, *The Observer's Handbook*, © 1968, 1969 Education Development Center, Inc., Newton, Mass. This publication is not endorsed by the copyright holder.

Observing Play

Number of males and females	Number of adults, juveniles, and infants	What Did You Observe?	How Did They Communicate?	What Things Did They Play With?	Additional Obervations

Observing Conflict

Number of males and females	Number of adults, juveniles, and infants	What Did You Observe?	How Did They Communicate?	How Did the Conflict End?	Additional Observations

Observing Eating Behavior

Number of males and females	Number of adults, juveniles, and infants	What Did You Observe?	What Were They Eating?	How Did They Get the Food?	Additional Observations

Field Notes
June 18

8:35. I entered the park. There are no baboons at LT. 8:55 on the Songora Ridge Road, there are widely separated trees full of baboons. Apparently the baboons slept here last night. A big male walked toward the car. We drove past him under the tree. Baboons let us come right under the tree!

We are sitting only four yards from this group and none pay attention to us. An older juvenile tried to approach the car two ~~BX~~ *or* three times. I finally discouraged him. *Songora Ridge: This troop will be the S.R. Troop.*

In the tree are three grooming pairs of juvenile$_2$ age. Two of the juveniles are wrestling quietly on stubby low branches. Three infant$_2$s keep crawling around the trunk to play and the juveniles pull their tails so they go back.

An older juvenile female on the lowest branch is cuddling one infant$_2$ in her arms and another is playing around her. A female with an infant$_2$ is coming down from the top of the tree and smacking her lips as she comes. This smacking the lips is ~~XXXX~~ really an in and out movement of the tongue between the lips making a smacking sound. It seems to be a way of expressing friendship or affection or of making other baboons peaceful. One adult male is 50 yards away, another under the tree being groomed by a young female, also an adult male in the tree. The male in the tree has a pointed nose. *We will call him "Needle Nose."*

The females with the young infants are staying near the adult males and are grooming them often. The adult males are very tolerant of the young infants; while I was watching just now one of the infants climbed up its mother as she groomed an adult male and sprawled over the male's muzzle. The male took no notice of this.

9:55. No movement on or around the tree or on the plain. One baboon just grunted and every baboon in the troop was instantly alert. A bark.

1:10. Most baboons still eating hungrily. In the past two hours I've seen the baboons eating a wide variety of ~~XXX~~ plants and grasses, perhaps 20 different types. One baboon just dug down 4" in hard soil to get roots and then ate them. This plain has a number of the whistling thorn trees (acacia d.) which the little baboons love to play in.

1:25. The baboons are still walking and eating. The infant$_1$ has not left Ma's chest at any time. It's a male, will name him Toto (Swahili for infant).

2:10. The troop, moving rapidly, is now to the "V" in Bushy Valley, almost in the heart of the LT group range (but I haven't seen the LT group). Left the SR group for a while to look for the LT group, looked at ~~4, 5~~ *4, 5* ~~Salt Lick~~ *Salt Lick* and ~~twelve two~~ but never found them.

When we returned at 2:40, found the SR group in the same place and ran over to them. One baboon is eating galls full of ants ~~BX~~ on the acacia trees. He throws away the outer husk, just eats the ants.

3:05. Ma, holding her infant, is being groomed by two infant$_2$s and a juvenile$_1$.

I think, since it takes too long to write out "Needle nose," I will call him the Swahili name for needle, "Sindano," or, better still, simply "Dano."

When she begins to walk Ma grabs Toto and pulls him to her, stands up holding him to her breast, then walks on giving him no more aid. Toto clings to her chest tightly. I have never seen an adult female aid an infant as it clings to her chest while she walks. What seems to happen when the infant becomes tired is that the infant lets go with the back feet and dangles for a moment from its front feet, which always causes the adult female to sit and let the infant nestle a while by her legs.

4:00. Play-fighting beginning among the infant$_2$s and juveniles. Through the afternoon XXXX none of the infant$_2$s have been with their mothers but have been in a close-knit group playing together. Now three infant$_2$s are playing together around the adult males using the males as blinds to hide behind and then strike out at each other.

4:45. Follows a count:

ad ♂↗	⊬⊬	
ad ♀	⊬⊬	
s/ ad ♂↗	'''	
s/ ad ♀	''	27 —
J̇$_2$	⊬⊬	should be
J̇$_1$	''	28
j$_2$	⊬⊬	

The baboons have eaten in the same spot for over an hour. Doing a good bit of digging, their cheek pouches nearly filled. Most of the baboons are eating the big roots we've seen them eating before. They dig down to free the root 4-8", then bend over and pull the root out with the teeth. It looks like XXXX a long, narrow carrot or radish. (Sample collected.) It takes 30 to 90 seconds to get the root up in this flint hard soil. I can't do it at all with my bare hands.

5:00. If a male sees a female, or a female sees a juvenile digging up one of the radish roots, the dominant animal will trot over, displace the other baboons, and finish digging up the root for himself. I've never seen an adult male displace another male for a root, though.

An infant$_2$ is now riding on Kink's back. Something suddenly frightened the troop and in two seconds they were 50 yards down the slope (the trees are in that direction). Two adult males, Deno and Kula (one with a scratched place on high right lower muzzle) XXXX remained in place looking steadily north. I can see nothing.

5:40. Grooming groups have formed, some grooming, some eating now. Since they were scared 40 minutes ago, the group has been feeding in a tight group and doing much grooming. Kink's infant started nursing when she sat down. She got up, he fell off, and gave a continuous ick, ick, ick, then low moans ("oooing") for several minutes.

5:55. Troop moving rapidly southeast in a line. Crossed the river at the first "L" in Valley of Lion Valley on the Mokoyeti River.

2

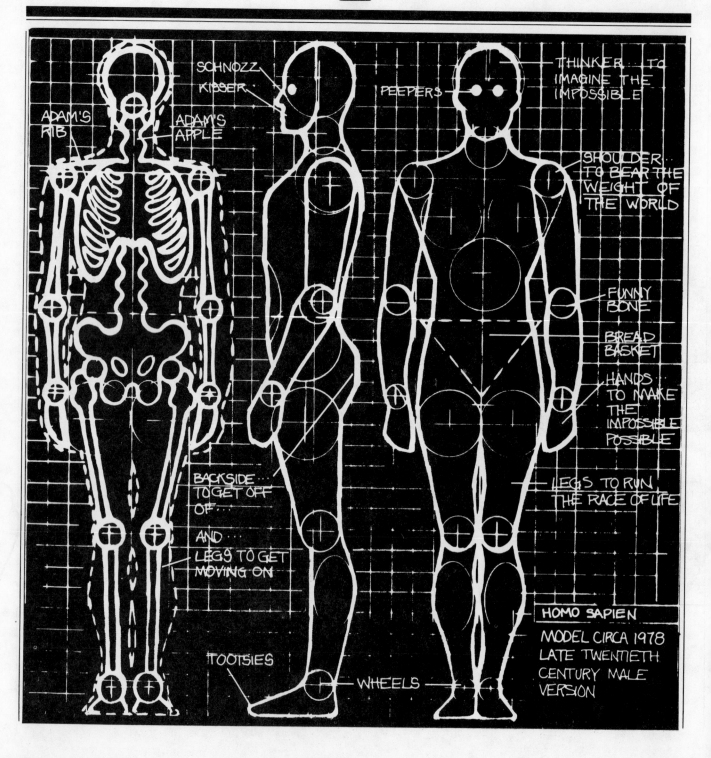

We're Only Human

Being a human is a wonderful experience. It begins at the moment of conception, when the father's sperm reaches the mother's egg. A new life. A new possibility. A new creation. Every moment in time brings us a new experience for growth. As humans, we have the potential for joy, happiness, and love. Sometimes we fall down. Sometimes we feel hurt, rejected, and unloved. But we learn to pick ourselves up and start anew. The process seems to repeat. As we grow older we see new possibilities for growth and love, but we also continue to face problems. In this chapter you will explore what it's like to be a human.

BIRTHING

Which of the following embryo drawings is a human?

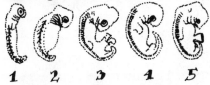

1   2   3   4   5

These are what the embryos of a shark, salamander, chicken, rat, and human look like after about 4 weeks of growth (we have written them in order). If you had difficulty identifying the human embryo, don't feel bad. At this stage of growth most vertebrate animals of different species look very much alike.

Here's another question for you to consider: Which of the following drawings of the human embryo is its actual size at 4 weeks of growth? Check your responses at the bottom of this page.

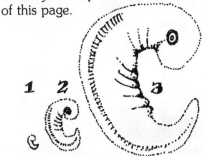

1   2   3

The process of birth for a human begins when the sperm from an adult male fertilizes the egg from an adult female. Each of us begins as a single cell, which then begins to divide again inside our mother's body.

We are going to give you an opportunity to discover how growing inside a safe, warm environment must feel. You also will learn about the stages of growth that we all go through up to that beautiful moment of birth. And, finally, you will interview your parents to find out about your birth.

Growth of the Human Embryo

You'll need a piece of clay about the size of your fist to do the activity.

The stages of growth for the human embryo are presented here in a scrambled order. Mold a piece of clay for each picture and try to place all the pieces in the correct order. After you've tried, check the key below.

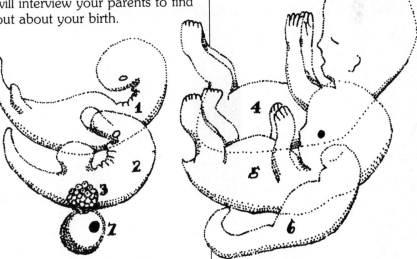

The embryo at the end of the stages shown here is only 12 weeks old, and it is about 3 cm long! By this time the embryo has developed a heart, and the skeletal system, eyes, legs, hands, and feet are forming. The embryo is now called a *fetus* and will continue to grow within the womb of the mother for another 24 weeks.

Being Born

Can you imagine the world you lived in before you were born? Every human shares this life. We all grew and developed within our mother and were born 9 months later. Let's recreate this world for ourselves.

For this activity find a partner, a bed sheet, and a quiet place. One of you should lie down under the sheet. The other person reads this fantasy trip in a slow and soothing voice.

Relax your body. . . . Stretch your limbs and begin to relax each part of

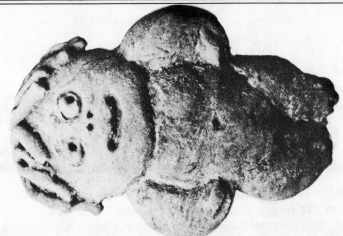

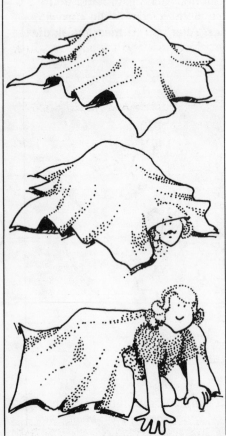

your body. . . . You are in a liquid environment, you are floating and weightless. . . . What is it like to be able to move and breathe in this environment? . . . Move your body slowly as you lie in this dark, warm environment. . . . Now listen to the sounds . . . that dull thumping sound of a heartbeat . . . your mother's heartbeat. . . . Now think about your food and nourishment. . . . Feel the food going from your mother to you through the umbilical cord. . . . How do you feel being nourished, never going hungry? . . . Now feel a smooth liquid covering your body. . . . You are moving your arms and legs through this liquid. . . . How does it feel? . . . Spend a few moments experiencing this feeling. . . . Now feel yourself beginning to move, to turn. . . . Your head is now next to a very tight spot. . . . Feel yourself pushing, squeezing, and beginning to move. . . . Begin to move your body slowly so that your head pokes out from the sheet. . . . Slowly open your eyes. . . . Continue to move until you completely emerge from the sheet. . . . Feel yourself being lifted slowly next to your partner, your head resting on your partner's chest. . . . You've made it. . . . Breathe in the beautiful air, listen to your partner's heartbeat. . . . You are born. . . . Slowly return to the here and now, and when you are ready, share your experience with your partner.

Reverse roles to give your partner the experience of birth.

Interviewing Your Parents About Your Birth

Now that you have some information about the growth and birth of the human embryo, you might be interested in getting some personal information from your own parents.

Not too many children do this, so when you talk with your mother and father explain to them that you want to know more about yourself and that they can be a great help to you. Here are some questions that you can use when you talk to your parents.

1. When did you find out that you were expecting me? How did you find out about it?
2. Could you feel me growing inside you? What did I do?
3. What was your life like when I was growing inside you? Did you have to change what you did?
4. Tell me about the day I was born. What was it like? What happened? Where was I born? When—in the morning, afternoon, or night?
5. Who was with you the moment I was born?
6. What did I do the moment I was born? Did I cry? Did I lie on your stomach?
7. How did you feel when I was born?
8. What were the days shortly after my birth like?
9. Oh, one other thing. Why did you give me this name?

From Birth to Death ...The Cycle of Life

One thing we share with all living things is the idea of a life cycle. Each plant or animal begins life, grows, reproduces, and dies. Here are some examples of how these take place. The offspring of each plant or animal follow the same cycle from generation to generation.

Studying Life Cycles
Plants
You'll need to obtain seeds (beans or radish seeds are good), potting soil, styrofoam cups, and pebbles. Plant two different types of seeds.

Make observations of the plants each day for the next month. How did each plant begin life? How did it grow and from what part? Did you see any evidence of reproduction? Did the plant die? If so, when?

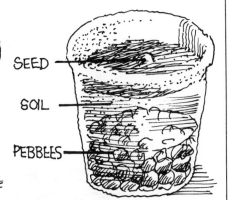

STYROFOAM CUP

SEED

SOIL

PEBBLES

Animals
Guppies are excellent animals to use to study the life cycle. You'll need to obtain an aquarium and a female and male guppy. Be sure to stock up on fish food, stones and pebbles, and water plants. Let the water sit for 48 hours before placing the guppies in the tank. Each day make observations of the guppies.

1. Could you tell when the female was pregnant?
2. How many baby guppies were born during the first pregnancy that you observed?
3. How many of those guppies lived?
4. How large did the guppies grow to be?
5. How long did your original guppies live?

Surveying Plants and Animals
All plants and animals have life cycles. You can learn more about this process by going outside and surveying the plants and animals in an area. Use the chart below to organize your thinking. We've listed some plants and animals for you to observe. Add others that are common to your local area.

Life Cycle Chart

Organism	Evidence of Birth	Evidence of Growth	Evidence of Maturity —Old Age	Evidence of Death
Human				
Bird	Eggs in nest beginning to crack open	Baby bird learning to fly	Birds building a nest	Bird lying on ground
Spider				
Pigeon				
Frog				
Ant				
Bush				
Grass				
Dandelion				
Tree				

Carl Rogers, American Psychologist (1902 -   )

Carl Rogers believes that every person is born with the desire to have a good self-opinion. He also believes that it is important for a person to grow up in an environment of warmth, love, understanding, and acceptance.

Rogers was born into a very religious but affectionate environment. His father was a successful businessperson. After high school, he studied agriculture but then turned toward theology. After studying religion, he shifted his interest to psychology and received his doctorate in this field in 1931.

As a young psychologist, Carl Rogers developed a theory about helping other humans that was very different from what most psychologists believed. Many people disagreed with and criticized his view, which was that all a person needed to solve a personal problem was the chance and freedom to do so. Rogers' theory has come to be known as the person-centered theory, and people have applied his ideas not only to counseling but to teaching, medicine, politics, and marriage. He has written many books, but his most important and perhaps most famous one is *On Becoming a Person.*

Thinking About Theory

1. *Carl Rogers believes that both children and adults deserve freedom to learn. The teacher should be a person who helps others learn, and trust in students and in the process of learning is the most important quality for a teacher to have. How do these ideas compare to your experience as a learner? How different would your school day be if Rogers' theory were used in your school?*

2. *Find someone you know, an adult or another child, who has been involved with a counselor or a psychologist.*

Ask this person if he or she will share with you some of the experiences of this situation.

3. *Interview some of your teachers or the principal about Carl Rogers' ideas. How do they feel about his view of learning?*

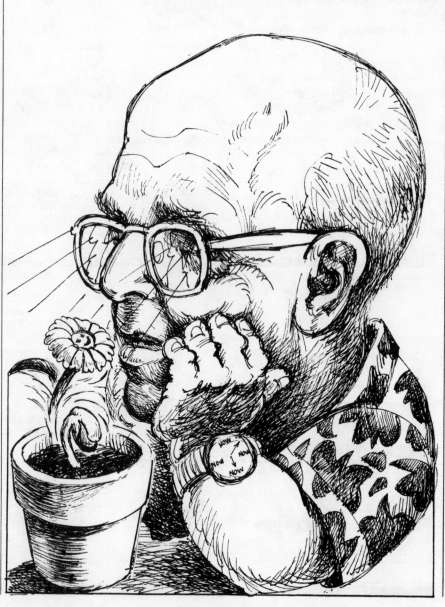

Abraham Maslow
—Humanistic Psychologist (1908–1970)

Abraham Maslow is known to many people as the founder of a new type of psychology. Other important types of psychology were developed by Sigmund Freud (1856–1939) and by John B. Watson (1878–1958).

Freud studied mentally disturbed people, and much of his theory was therefore based on the study of sick people. He believed that the way a person behaved was determined at a very early age. A "good" person held in all impulses, while a "bad" person enjoyed them. His technique was called psychoanalysis. The patient would relax on a couch and talk about whatever entered his or her mind and about dreams. Freud's goal in this treatment was to reduce guilt and conquer mental illness in people.

The type of psychology developed by Watson is called behaviorism. Many other people have contributed to our understanding of behaviorism. The most famous is probably B. F. Skinner, a professor at Harvard University. The behaviorists put great stress on stimulus-response learning as the chief way that humans learn. Because of this they study very carefully the environment outside the human being.

Maslow thought differently about human beings. Freud studied the sick. Maslow said we must study the healthy. His third-force psychology is unique because his proposed subjects for study were the very best human beings he thought he could find— loving, caring, playful, honest, growing, and old. He felt that he could learn a great deal about the human species by studying what he called the "growing tip." He also referred to these humans as self-actualizing humans. Some of the people Maslow studied were Ruth Benedict, Abraham Lincoln, Thomas Jefferson, Albert Einstein, Eleanor Roosevelt, Jane Addams, Albert Schweitzer, and William James.

One of the most important aspects of Maslow's theory is that it is one of hope. He maintained that humans do have values and are creative. We can solve problems and can be healthy. To do this, we must live in a culture that values cooperation, love, creativity, and growth. Maslow led the way to the development of humanistic psychology.

Thinking About Maslow

1. Maslow believed that humans are motivated to fulfill our needs for love, self-esteem, and self-realization along with our needs for food, air, water, and safety. What do you think about this theory?

2. Maslow also developed the idea that some people did fulfill their highest needs. These self-actualized people tended to be very accepting of others, creative, open to change, spontaneous, sometimes privacy seeking, and able to have many rich experiences. These people were older than most of us. Can you think of some older people that you know or have read about that are self-actualizing persons? Interview or read about them to find out what they are like.

3. Maslow spoke and wrote about the need humans have for love. What does the word "love" mean to you? In what ways do you show your love for other people, places, and things that you do?

Peek-a-boo Actions

Peek-a-boo is a game that we play throughout life. Each of us peeks out at the world. We reveal to others who we think we are, hoping each time to be accepted. Each time we are accepted we feel good about ourselves, and the image we have of ourselves is reinforced. This image is our self-concept, and that's what peek-a-boo actions are all about.

Following is a collection of activities that will help you think about your self-concept and reinforce it. Each activity is an encounter with either yourself or with others. As you participate in these actions, remember that you have the power to be kind, helpful, decent, affectionate, and warm toward others. Each time that you are, you help another person develop a healthy self-image.

Personal Journal

A journal is a book in which you write about your thoughts and feelings. You can use words, pictures, drawings, poems, cartoons, and so forth. You can make your own journal by binding sheets of paper together and covering them with water-resistant decorative wallpaper. You can also purchase one in a bookstore. Each day give yourself the gift of 20 minutes to write in your journal. Here are some sentence starters for inspiration: Today I liked, I disliked, I felt, I wish, I got angry when, My parents, I visited, I was surprised, I learned that.

Me and My Music

Today's music is a beautiful way to express your thoughts and feelings about yourself, other people, things, places, and ideas. Following are a number of value areas that you probably think about from time to time: love, school, friends, war, peace, sex, future, sorrow, joy, animals, nature,

religion, personal tastes, culture, family, divorce, and death.

Select a value area and find a song from your collection of records or tapes that you feel expresses for you the meaning of the value area, both in the words and music. If you do this in a group, each member can bring in a different song. You can also listen to songs and identify value areas in the words and music. How do the composer's thoughts compare to your own?

I'm OK

This works best as a group activity. On a large sheet of paper, list all the behaviors that you think are OK but that others might think are bad. Share these lists with your group. As you discuss each behavior, check with others in the group to see if they think the behavior is bad. You might discover that others think your behavior is OK.

Body Art

On large sheets of paper, draw the outlines of your body and those of others in a group. Use colors, words, or magazine pictures to describe how you feel about various

parts of your body. After each person has completed his or her outline, discuss your interpretations with each other.

My Self × 6

Gather five friends to form a group of six. One at a time, spend 6 minutes telling the rest of the group who you are, what the most important experience in your life was, and what the happiest experience in your life was. If you don't use the 6 minutes, other group members should ask you questions. After each person has had 6 minutes, spend about 10 minutes discussing your reactions to the process.

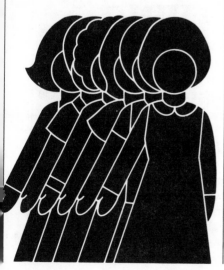

Once A Week

In your journal, write down the high points of the week. Include things like when you were empathic (accepting), when others strongly agreed or disagreed with you, how

the week could have been better for you, and what you still have left to do.

Situations

What do you do in situations like the following? Write your reactions in your journal and share them with a small group of friends.

1. A person you do not like punches you hard but says that it was an accident.

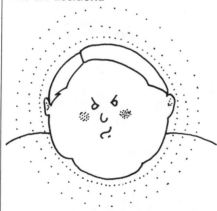

2. You spill paint remover on your parents' new coffee table while painting a model airplane.
3. You lent a person money 3 weeks ago, and you now need it desperately.
4. Your baby brother breaks your favorite record.
5. Your boyfriend or girlfriend tells you that you have bad breath.
6. You step on the dog's intestinal mess as you enter your friend's home but don't discover it until you are at the dinner table.

7. You are at summer camp and feel very lonely.
8. Your best friend tells you that he or she is moving to another state.

One Picture Or a Thousand Words

This activity is fun to do with a group. Everyone gets a large sheet of paper, pens, crayons, and string. Each of you should draw or write one of the following suggestions, and tie the paper around your neck with string:

1. Draw a picture, caricature, or cartoon of yourself.
2. Make a pie graph of yourself with your distribution of love, energy, and talents.
3. Draw a picture of the important events in your life.
4. Write words that describe yourself.

Spend about ten minutes milling about the room looking at each other's signs. What did each of you learn about yourself?

All the Difference in the World

Being human means being different from everyone else. Differences sometimes lead to problems such as prejudice. We would like to celebrate our differences and to view them as important in their own right. In this activity you will have a chance to "differentiate" between differences that are based on the environment we grow up in and those that are based on heredity.

Environment

Each of us has grown up in a different environment. Even children that grow up in the same family experience different environments. Environment includes not only the physical setting that we live in but the behaviors of the other people within it, too. Environment has an influence on our preferences for food, clothing, religion, education, and career.

List on the preference chart on page 21, your preference in each area. Then list the preferences of one of your friends (you may have to check with him or her to be sure that you are accurate). After your chart is complete, discuss the list with your friend and try to explain your preferences. Your family's preferences might be one explanation. How different and alike are the two of you?

This activity gives you a clue that many of the differences among people are related to their environment. What do you think you would be like if you grew up in any of these groups? How do you imagine children from any of these groups would react to living in your family?

Southwest American Indian tribe
Eskimo family in Northern Alaska
Black family in Nigeria, Africa
Chinese family in Peking, China

Heredity

No two people with the same

fingerprints have ever been found. The general pattern may be similar, but the specific details of the lines differ for each person. Which of the thumbprint patterns is similar to yours? To find out, get an ink pad and make a print of your right thumb (roll your thumb over the pad from left to right, then roll your thumb in the box provided).

Now, put your finger on this fact: Differences in thumbprints are caused by the unique ways our bodies grow and develop, not by the environment. This is where our parents come in! At the moment of conception, each of our parents passes on to us the genes that will determine many of our qualities: eye and hair color, nose shape, foot size, ear lobe structure, and even thumbprint pattern.

Let's take a look at some physical characteristics that heredity is responsible for. The drawings show five different characteristics that people either have or do not have. For example, a person is either a tongue roller or is not one. Find out if your friends have any of these characteristics. Record your data on the chart on page 21.

Can you explain why individuals have any of these characteristics? For each characteristic that is present in you, think about which of your parents has the same characteristic.

THE REAL THING

We're not talking about something to quench your thirst, we're inviting you to play a real game. The Real Thing is a game for four to six players. Everyone is a winner in this game because the object is self-growth. The game ends *only* when everyone has reached the Growth Center.

Materials

Low and *High Risk* cards, cut out from Appendix and placed on gameboard

Two 3 × 5 index cards for each player, one labeled Growth and the other, Safety

1 set of dice

Goal of the Game

The purpose of this game is to grow by taking risks to reach the Growth Center. Each player competes against him- or herself, choosing to behave in front of the other players in either a growth- or safety-oriented way. Are you willing

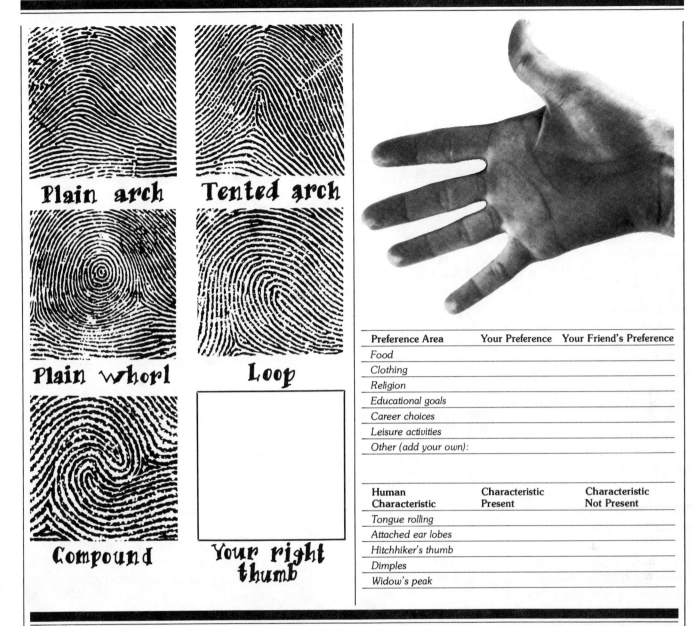

Plain arch

Tented arch

Plain whorl

Loop

Compound

Your right thumb

Preference Area	Your Preference	Your Friend's Preference
Food		
Clothing		
Religion		
Educational goals		
Career choices		
Leisure activities		
Other (add your own):		

Human Characteristic	Characteristic Present	Characteristic Not Present
Tongue rolling		
Attached ear lobes		
Hitchhiker's thumb		
Dimples		
Widow's peak		

to grow or do you want to play it safe? Players draw cards that describe risk situations and then respond as directed. The other players then vote to decide if the response was growth- or safety-oriented.

How to Play

1. *Each player selects a path. The group then decides who goes first.*

2. *This player selects the top card from the Low Risk deck. The player reads the card aloud so that all players know what the card says. The player has 30 seconds to decide how to respond to the statement on the card, then acts or behaves in*
front of the group.

3. *When the player has completed the behavior, the other players independently decide if the player acted in a growth- or safety-oriented manner. To vote, each player turns over either the Growth or Safety index card.*

4. *At this point, the player rolls the dice. If the majority of the players voted Growth, the player moves ahead the full count on the dice; if the majority voted Safety, the player moves only half the count.*

5. *At this point, the player can ask the others to explain their vote.*

6. *The game proceeds with the*
next player on the left selecting a Low Risk card. Players pick Low or High Risk cards to match the zone they land in. The game ends when all players reach the Growth Center.

Special Notes

WARNING: Do not play this game unless you are willing to be honest with yourself and other group members. This game is the real thing.

Blank risk cards: Make several blank *Low* and *High Risk* cards. After you've played the game, make up your own risk situations.

3

Brain Power

Many people are beginning to realize that the most amazing and mysterious part of the universe might well be the human brain. Only over a thousand cubic centimeters in volume, it packs a lot of power. The brain has the power to do all of the following and much more:

1. Store millions of "bits" of information
2. Create new images
3. Coordinate the motions and reactions of a magnificent machine—the human body
4. Express a wide variety of emotions and feelings
5. Communicate
6. Solve problems
7. Control the inner workings of the mind through biofeedback
8. Translate the reactions of our senses into messages that we can understand.

In this section you will find ideas and activities to help you become more aware of and sensitive to your own brain power. Have fun exploring your own thinker!

How Little Kids Use Their Thinkers

Here are several activities that will help you understand how humans learn in their early years. Watching babies with their parents, observing babies by themselves, and playing simple games with young children will provide you with some clues about how children learn.

Babies and Parents

Watch a baby with one of its parents. On a chart like the one shown here, record what the parent does or says that might teach the baby something. Later, write down what the baby might be learning from the parent.

Babies Learning Alone

Watch a baby playing alone or with several other babies. Make a list of things you think the babies have learned that no one has purposely taught them.

1. Ask several parents if their children did the things on your list. Did the parents teach their babies these things?

2. Compare your list with the lists made by friends.

3. Look in books for pictures of babies in other parts of the world doing the same things.

4. What have you learned to do that no one has taught you?

Parent's Actions	Parent's Words	What the Baby Might Be Learning
Giving the baby a rattle and moving baby's head back and forth	"Shake the rattle."	How to grasp an object
Holding baby in arms and looking directly at baby with a great deal of excitement	"Ma-ma," "ma-'ma."	How to speak

Adapted from Man: A Course of Study, The Observers Handbook, © 1968, 1969 Education Development Center, Inc., Newton, Mass. Used with permission. This publication is not endorsed by the original copyright holder.

Thinking Games

Another way to find out about young children's learning is to play some games with them. Each task shown here is a type of game you can play with young children. Very young children are able to do most of the tasks, but they may give you answers that are very different from our ways of thinking. This is not because they are stupid or lack intelligence but because of their level of intellectual development.

Ask two young children about 5 and 8 years old whether they would like to play some fun games with you. Do the tasks separately with each child. Do not let the children hear each other's answers. Be sure to follow these directions carefully when you explain the task to each child. Notice that each task requires you to do two things: first, to demonstrate something to the child and ask the child to respond to the demonstration; second, to ask the child why he or she responded that way. Remember, the child's response is not wrong. Find a place, on the floor or at a table, where you will not be disturbed.

Thinking Game Thoughts

1. How did the children's responses to the tasks differ?

2. Did the older child respond more often in ways similar to your own thinking? Why?

3. How do you think boys and girls of your own age would respond to these tasks?

1

Thinking Game Conserving Volume

Materials: *2 jars (one tall and skinny, the other short and fat) and colored water (or juice, for an after-task refreshment).*

Instructions for Task: *Show the child the two jars, with the water in the short one. Ask, "What will happen if I pour the water into the tall jar? Will I have more, less, or the same amount?" After the child answers, pour the water into the tall container. Now ask again if there is more, less, or the same amount of water.*

Justification Question: *Ask the child why the amount of water is more, less, or the same.*

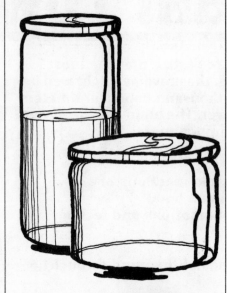

2

Thinking Game Conserving Matter

Materials: *Play dough or clay.*
Instructions for Task: *Show the child a ball of clay the size of a tennis ball. After the child has observed the ball, roll it into a cylinder. Then ask the*

child if the cylinder (call it a snake or hot dog) has more, less, or the same amount of clay as the ball.

Justification Question: *Ask the child why the snake has more, less, or the same amount of clay as the ball.*

3

Thinking Game Conserving Length

Materials: *2 narrow strips of paper (cut into four equal lengths) and 2 small toy cars.*

Instructions for Task: *Show the child the strips of paper as indicated in A.*

Move the paper strips as shown in B.

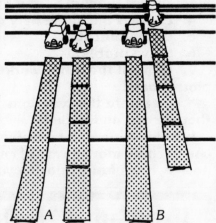

Ask the child if two cars starting a race at one end (point to the cars) and traveling at the same speed would both finish the race at the end of the track (point to the ends of the paper strips) at the same time.

Justification Question: *Ask why the child thinks so. Rearrange a segmented straw as shown below and ask the same question you did before.*

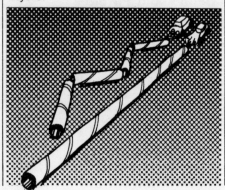

Thinking Game
Displacement

4

Materials: Tall cylinder, rubber band, colored water, and two blocks of identical size but very different weight that will sink (you can use any pair of objects as long as they are the same shape and size but different weight).

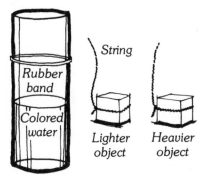

String

Rubber band

Colored water

Lighter object

Heavier object

Instructions for Task: Give the child both objects and ask which is heavier. Ask the child what will happen to the level of water if the lighter object is lowered into the cylinder. Have the child place the rubber band where he or she thinks the water level will move to.

Gently lower the lighter block into the water. Have the child move the rubber band to the level of the water. Remove the lighter object. Now ask the child where the water level will move to if the heavier object is lowered into the cylinder. Will the level be higher, lower, or the same?

Justification Question: Ask the child why the water level will be as he or she thinks. Now, lower the object into the water.

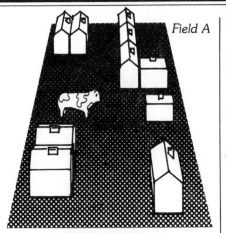

Field A

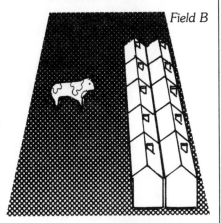

Field B

Thinking Game
Conserving Area

5

Materials: 2 identical pieces of construction paper, 20 houses (a Monopoly game is a good source for these) or blocks, and 2 toy animals.

Instructions for Task: Point out to the child that the pieces of paper represent fields of grass and are of identical size. Because they are the same size, the animal on each will have the same amount of grass to eat. Place the houses or blocks on the fields as shown above and tell the child that they are barns.

Now ask which animal will have the most grass to eat (or whether each amount of grass will be the same).

Justification Question: Ask why the child thinks the answer to be true. Continue adding one barn to each field in the patterns shown in the illustrations. Each time ask, "Which animal will have the most grass to eat?"

Resting the Mind

When we are awake, our minds are constantly thinking, taking in the sounds and sights of the environment. In recent years, more people in Western cultures have become interested in the techniques for controlling the mind that are used in the Far East. One very important aspect of mind control is meditation, a method that many people in the Far East exercise. Meditation leads one to a state of no-mind, void, or nothingness. It is a state of consciousness in which the mind is thinking—about nothing. Most of the disciplines that practice meditation, such as Zen, Yoga, and Sufi, involve concentration on an object, sound, or movement. Here are two exercises you may wish to try.

Exercise 1: Counting Your Breaths

In this meditation exercise you will be counting the exhalations of your breath. Sit comfortably and each time you breath out, count mentally. Count up to ten and then repeat the

process. A variation is to include an "and" between counts to fill up the space between exhalations. Thus, count "one" for the first exhalation, "and" for the next inhalation, "two" for the next exhalation, "and" for the next inhalation, and so forth. Do this for 15 minutes for the first 2 weeks, then increase to 20 minutes.

Exercise 2: The Bubble

Imagine yourself sitting at the bottom of a lake. Picture each thought, feeling, and perception that comes into your mind as a bubble rising into the space above you, passing through it and out of sight. When you have a thought, simply observe it for 5 to 8 seconds until it passes out of your visual space. The process helps you maintain a definite timing, and you concentrate on only one thing at a time. Start with 10 minutes for 2 weeks. After some practice, you may wish to transform your thoughts into puffs of smoke or logs.

Two Brains?

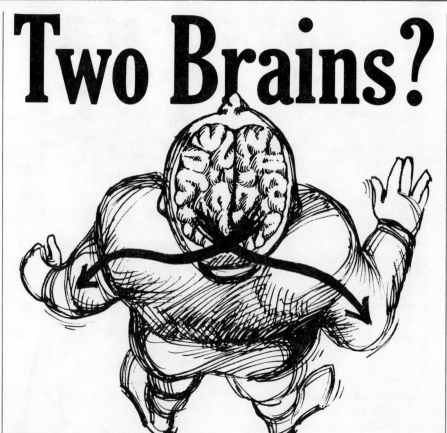

Did you ever think that you might have two brains instead of one? In the past few years, some scientists have developed a theory that the two hemispheres, or halves, of the brain are responsible for very different kinds of thinking.

To get in touch with these two different ways of thinking, have someone read the following paragraph to you as you close your eyes:

Try to sense each side of your body. Tune into the feelings of the left and right sides, including strengths and weaknesses. I'm going to ask you several questions. Reflect on each question and search inside yourself for the answer. Which side of you is more feminine? Which side is more masculine? Which do you consider the dark side? Which is the light side? Which side is more logical? Which is more intuitive? Which side is more artistic? Now think about which of the questions you answered with your right side. Slowly come back to the room and open your eyes.

You probably found that the right side of your body was masculine, light, and logical, while your left side was feminine, dark, intuitive, and artistic. A theory that scientists have developed to explain this is the split-brain theory. Their discoveries about how we think suggest that the human brain has two distinct kinds of thinking capabilities: the intuitive and aesthetic, and the logical and rational. These two thinking abilities appear to originate in different halves of the brain. Intuitive and aesthetic thinking originates in the right hemisphere, while logical and rational thinking originates in the left hemisphere. Following are two lists of activities humans do, classified under the appropriate half of the brain.

Left Hemisphere Thinking	Right Hemisphere Thinking
Analyzing	Feeling
Classifying	Dreaming
Writing	Loving
Ordering	Drawing
Reasoning	Imagining
Reading	Singing
Planning	
Measuring	

Ivan Pavlov (1849-1936): The Conditioned Reflex

Pavlov was born in a small town in central Russia. He was a man with much enthusiasm and energy and a bright mind. Becoming interested in the physiology of blood circulation, he later did research on digestion and received the Nobel Prize for it in 1904.

Pavlov is most famous for the experiments he did with dogs. He trained a dog to salivate at the sound of a bell, and his remarkable discovery was that some reflexes such as gastric secretions may be psychologically conditioned. This, to a physiologist, was a surprising idea. Pavlov had the genius to do more research on his theory, and he is credited with opening up an entire field of psychology —the study of conditioned reflexes.

Reflex Reflection

1. Do a survey in your class, school, or neighborhood to find out if people have ever heard of Pavlov and what they know about him.

2. What do you think controls conditioned reflexes?

3. Pavlov did most of his early work in a primitive wood building much like a shed. He paid for most of his research from his small salary. What type of "working" conditions do you have? How do you get the money to do the things you want to do?

Jean Piaget
PSYCHOLOGIST(1896–)

Jean Piaget is a famous Swiss psychologist who has devoted more than 50 years to the study of how children learn. He has helped us discover that children's thinking is creative, develops in stages, and is a lifelong process.

Piaget is a very disciplined man. Every morning he gets up at 4:00 A.M. and writes about his research. He teaches in the morning and takes long walks in the afternoon. In the summer he goes to the Alps and writes about the research on thinking that he and his assistants have done. Piaget has written over fifty books and hundreds of articles.

Pondering About Piaget

1. Piaget takes long walks so that he can think about the problems he is working on. How do you try to solve problems you have? Do you give yourself this time alone?

2. Children who are 5 to 8 years old are in a thinking stage that Piaget calls concrete thinking. Look back at the thinking games in the How Little Kids Use Their Thinkers section. Do you think these games are examples of concrete or abstract thinking?

Using Guinea Pigs in Psychology

FIRST, YOU MUST "CARE"

Briefly, the requirements for animal care are adequate food and water, clean and dry litter, warm surroundings, adequate exercise space, and gentle handling.

The food should be supplied either continually or at regular intervals in sufficient quantity and variety to maintain weight and health. Put it into a feeding container and add to it as needed. Suitable food for guinea pigs is rabbit food, pellets, or other food that a local pet shop or veterinarian recommends. You may also supplement their diet with rolled oats, greens, apples, carrots, sweet potatoes, fresh grass, or alfalfa hay.

Continually supply your guinea pigs with fresh water in a container that cannot easily be tipped or dirtied. We recommend a watering bottle. Use one that is designed so that air bubbles will not interfere with the flow of water.

Periodic cleaning of the cage (at least once a week) and regular replacement of the litter on the bottom of the cage will keep the litter clean and dry.

Guinea pigs are more susceptible to colds when they have been subjected to sudden temperature

and humidity changes or drafts. Thus, avoid temperatures that deviate greatly from normal room temperature. Do not place the cage in direct sunlight. If the temperature of the room is lowered overnight or on weekends during the cold months, supply extra heat by operating an electric light (100 to 150 watts) near the cage. You might also insulate the cage with a cardboard box.

Have a pen that is large enough for the animals to exercise in, or let them exercise in the room at intervals during the day. A space of $30 \times 40 \times 60$ cm is recommended for each guinea pig.

Guinea pigs are healthy and hardy creatures. You can usually handle them without worrying about being bitten or scratched. Do handle them gently and not excessively, however. You should be at ease with the animals and they with you if they are to be unafraid and perform well in a maze. Handle the guinea pigs gently several times a day for 2 weeks before you have them learn a maze.

Research Certificate

Before doing any experiments with guinea pigs or other animals, please read and sign the certificate. If you do a study in which the subjects are humans, inform them of the purpose of your study and of how you will use the results. Obtain their permission either orally or in writing.

EXPERIMENTING WITH ANIMALS CERTIFICATE

I have read the following statements and agree with the idea that animals should be treated humanely.

1. I have read about how to care for animals.
2. My study does not and will not include malicious treatment of animals.
3. I agree to report to others the actual methods and results of my experiments.

_____   _____
Signed   **Date**

Guinea pig activities are from *Science: A Process Approach.* Copyright © 1967 by the American Association for the Advancement of Science. Published by Xerox.

Making Two A-Mazing Things

Here are two plans for a maze, each requiring a large box at least 1 × 1.3 m (3 × 4 ft.) with walls 30 cm (12 in.) high. The passages in the maze should be at least 10 cm wide so that the animals can move freely without becoming excited or frightened. Arrange the maze with several locations at which the guinea pigs must choose between a path that leads to the food by the most direct route, a path that leads to the food by a longer or slower route, and a path that leads to a dead end. Do not make the maze pattern too difficult.

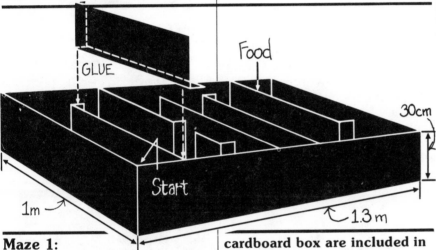

Maze 1:
   The panels of this maze are cut from various sizes of cardboard. Note that one corner and part of the bottom of the cardboard box are included in order to make a more rigid panel. Attach the sections to the large box with glue or masking tape.

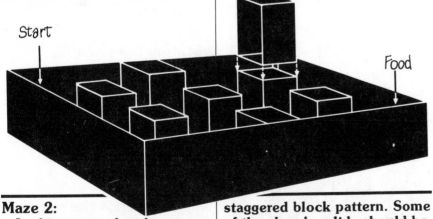

Maze 2:
   In this maze, shoe boxes are glued or taped to the bottom of the large box to form a staggered block pattern. Some of the shoe box lids should be taped on and other lids removed to form blind turns.

The A-Mazing Guinea Pigs

The experiments described here do not directly measure guinea pig learning; they focus on the behavior of guinea pigs in a maze. Observations include measurement of the time it takes a guinea pig to go through a maze. If the time decreases with each trial, you can probably infer that the guinea pig has "remembered" the path from previous trials.

General Guinea Pig Procedure
   1. Start your experiments with two guinea pigs.
   2. Do not feed your guinea pigs for at least 12 hours before each experiment. After each trial, let the animals eat whatever food you have put in the maze and return them to their cage with adequate food for the rest of the day.
   3. Let one guinea pig smell the food. Then put the food at the end of the maze and the guinea pig in the starting passageways.

TRIAL NUMBER	MAZE TIME GUINEA PIG A
1	3 MIN 0 SEC
2	1 MIN 0 SEC
3	1 MIN 20 SEC
4	30 SEC
5	25 SEC
6	18 SEC
7	35 SEC
8	25 SEC
9	17 SEC

TRIAL NUMBER	MAZE TIME GUINEA PIG B
1	13 MIN 0 SEC
2	2 MIN 0 SEC
3	3 MIN 0 SEC
4	4 MIN 0 SEC
5	40 SEC
6	1 MIN 0 SEC
7	15 SEC
8	13 SEC
9	12 SEC

4. Note the starting time and observe the animal making its first trial run through the maze. When the animal reaches the food, note the time again and compute the maze time. Record it in a table like the ones shown here. Repeat the trial for the second guinea pig.

5. Do at least six or seven trials with both guinea pigs, recording the maze time for each trial. Conduct the trials at the same time every day or every 2 days.

6. Using your data, make a bar graph to show the results of your experiment.

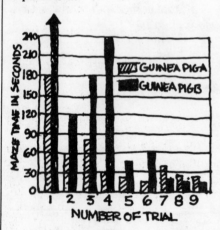

Rating Your Results

1. If you ran another trial beyond the data you collected, what maze time would you predict for each guinea pig?

2. Are female guinea pigs smarter than male guinea pigs?

3. Why did the maze time tend to become shorter and shorter?

4. Why did the maze time not change much after five or six trials?

5. Have the guinea pigs learned?

MEALWORM LEARNING

Mealworms, which are beetles in the larva stage, are well suited for studies of animal behavior. Mealworms live in dark, damp places such as piles of grain in mills. Four or five handfuls of bran or cereal flakes will support 500 mealworms for many weeks. A piece of potato or apple will provide mealworm water requirements. A healthy mealworm is a happy mealworm, and your mealworms are now ready for experiments!

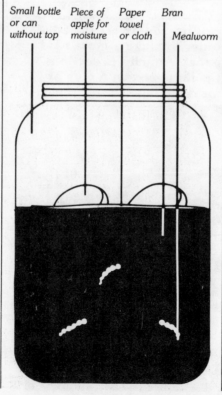

Small bottle or can without top *Piece of apple for moisture* *Paper towel or cloth* *Bran*

Mealworm

How Do Mealworms Sense?

Do mealworms see? Do they sense objects with their entire bodies? To find out, study how mealworms follow walls. Matchsticks, toothpicks, popsicle sticks, and tongue depressors make very good walls for mealworms. Here are some ways to arrange and build walls.

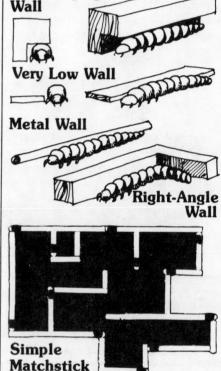

Overhanging Wall

Very Low Wall

Metal Wall

Right-Angle Wall

Simple Matchstick Maze of Walls

Locating Bran in a Box

Place a pile of bran near one end of a shoe box. Place about ten mealworms near the other end. As the mealworms move, trace their paths with a pencil but be careful not to touch them.

1. Do the mealworms seem able to go straight to the bran after they get close?

2. Are mealworm paths different if bran is replaced by sawdust?

3. Does the distance traveled by a mealworm on later trials become shorter?

4. *If you made two piles, one along the edge and the other in the middle, which one would the mealworm go for?*

5. *What paths do mealworms make in the dark? (Use talcum powder on the bottom of the box.)*

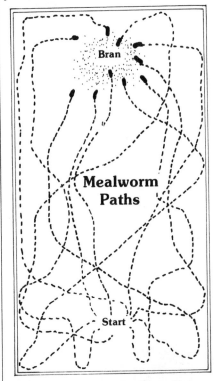

Mealworm Paths

Mealworm Preference for Color

Place about five mealworms on a white disc surrounded by four different colored squares. What color do the mealworms prefer?

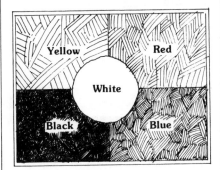

Exploring a Box

Place ten mealworms in the center of a shoe box. Observe the behavior of the mealworms. Do mealworms explore in groups or individually? Do they climb up or

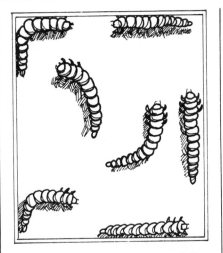

along walls? Do they give up? Do they try to get out or do they prefer staying in?

Find out how many seconds mealworms spend on the following activities: stopping, moving along the bottom of the box, moving along the edges, climbing up the sides, climbing up corners, and moving in corners.

Behavior in a T Maze

Construct a T maze using tongue depressors or cardboard to look like this diagram. Previous experiments have shown that the direction the mealworm turns at the T choice point is related to the direction of the forced turn. Design an experiment to find out if there is such a relationship.

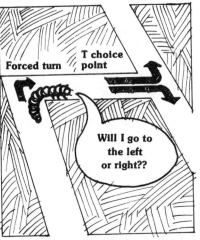

What's Your Maze Time?

With the eraser end of a pencil, trace your way through this maze. Write down your starting and ending times. Repeat the experiment at the same time on successive days.

Try this maze on your friends, parents, and brothers or sisters. How do your times compare to theirs?

By the way, what have you learned by doing this experiment?

Optical Illusions

Can you see the images of both a young woman and an old lady in this drawing? The way the mind interprets lines determines our perception of the environment. Have some of your friends look at the illustration. What do they "see"?

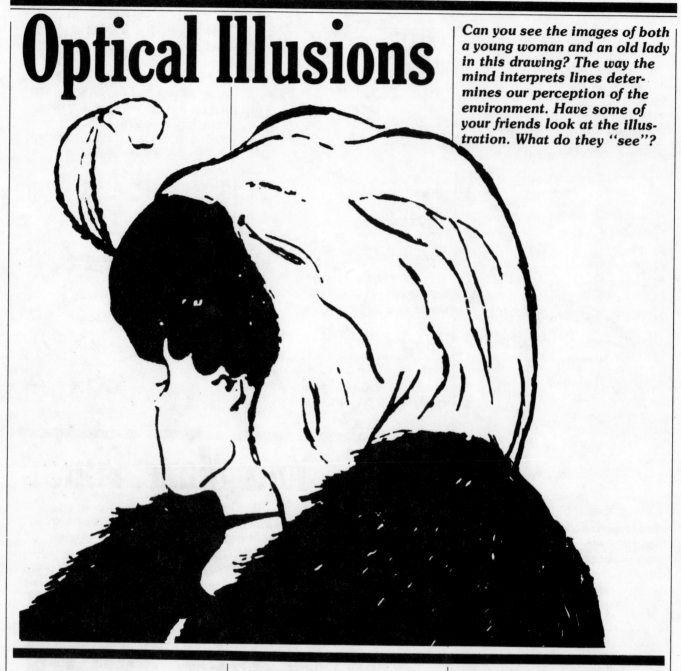

Which Is Bigger?

Our perception of objects and events sometimes differs from reality. Focus on the small figures in the two illustrations. How are they different?
If you measured them with a ruler, you know that they are the same size. But even knowing that, when you look back at the pictures, they still look different in size.

Look at the diagram of the three girls. Which do you think is tallest? Which do you think is shortest?

Do you think you were fooled? Measure all three girls with a ruler. Well, sometimes we aren't always right! Show the same illustration to some of your friends. How do you think they will do?

Two Brain Teasers

Connect all dots with 4 straight lines without lifting your pencil.

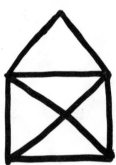

Reproduce this figure without lifting your pencil or crossing lines. Check your solutions against the ones in the Appendix.

Arrow Puzzler

Here is another puzzler. Which part of the line segment looks longer, A or B?

You can make an optical illusion device that can be used to study the double-arrow illustration. All you need are two white cards or two small pieces of paper.

Follow This "Straight and Arrow" Procedure

1. Fold each card and draw whole and partial arrows, as shown here.

2. Place card B over card A so that card A will slide in and out.

3. Adjust the card so that the two arrows are exactly the same size. On the other side of card A, draw a vertical line along the edge formed by card B. This line will allow you to measure how much other people are fooled by the illusion.

Now you are ready to do some tests of perception. Have your test subject stand about 2 m from you as you hold up the card. Start with the card out as far as possible. Slowly move the card in until the subject tells you that the two lines are equal. Measure the distance from the line on the back of card A to the edge of card B and record it on a sheet of paper or on the table provided at the right.

Repeat the experiment, but this time start with the card in; slowly move the card out until the subject tells you to stop.

Adapted from Intermediate Science Curriculum Study, *Investigating Variation* (Mornstown, N.J.: Silver Burdett, 1972). © 1972 Florida State University.

Perception Test Data		
sub ject	Trial 1 Going In	Trial 2 Going Out
1		
2		
3		
4		
5		
6		
7		
8		
9		
10		

4

People Power

Have you ever heard the word "anthropology"? Anthropology is the study of the ways that groups of human beings are the same and yet different. If you are a curious person and are interested in finding out about what makes us different from animals, what we have in common with animals, how people in different parts of the world get along or fight with each other, how people communicate with each other, and many, many other amazing earthpeople characteristics, then you will probably enjoy the activities in this chapter. Come along and learn about people power.

Margaret Mead, Anthropologist

(1901–   )

Margaret Mead was raised in a home in which both her father and mother encouraged her to think for herself. Her father was a professor at the University of Pennsylvania. Her mother was a sociologist (a scientist who studies how groups of people behave) who believed that women should have the same freedom and opportunities as men. Margaret Mead grew up with this belief in women's rights.

In college, she had a strong interest in psychology but also became interested in the field of anthropology. In 1925 she decided to go to the Pacific island of Samoa to study the life of teen-age native girls. Many people advised her not to go because they thought that such an adventure wasn't proper for a young woman. She went anyway.

Dr. Mead has had a very active career as a writer, lecturer, and teacher. Her interest in the problems of racial groups, in the relationships between young people and adults, and in many other areas has stayed with her all through life. Her first book, *Coming of Age in Samoa* (1928), was based on her experiences living with the Samoans. Her many other books include *Anthropologists and What They Do, A Way of Seeing,* and *Rap on Race.* In her autobiography, *Blackberry Winter,* she wrote:

What is there for young anthropologists to do today? In one sense, everything. The best possible work has not yet been done. If I were 21 today, I would elect to join the communicating network of these young people the world over who recognize the urgency of life-supporting change. There is hope, I believe, in seeing the human

adventure as a whole and in the shared trust that knowledge about mankind, sought in reverence for life, can bring life.

More on Margaret Mead

1. What do you think about this quote from her autobiography? Would you like to be an anthropologist? Do you think, as she does, that there is hope?

2. If you were Margaret Mead, do you think that you would have gone to a Pacific island to study the ways in which its people lived? If you did go, what things would you have been interested in learning about?

3. Many people think that the women's movement is a new idea. What do you think Dr. Mead would say if you asked her about it?

4. Do you think that we can learn much about ourselves by studying the way in which other people live? Why or why not?

B

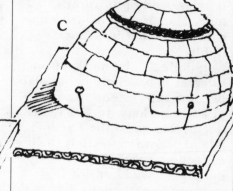

Building Your Own Igloo

In this project, you'll be able to go through some of the same steps that an Eskimo goes through to build an igloo.

As you build your igloo, be very careful not to cut yourself with the razor blade. If you do not have an X-acto knife to use, be sure to use a single-edge razor blade instead.

Materials
1 styrofoam ice bucket
1 bottle of white glue
1 X-acto knife
1 injector razor blade
Straight pins
Corrugated paper or board
Heavy thread
Needle

Procedure for a N-ice Igloo

1. Using the razor blade or the X-acto knife, cut the rim from the styrofoam bucket as shown in A and pin it to the corrugated paper or board. The rim of the bucket should tilt slightly toward the inside.

A

X

From Man: A Course of Study, *The Netsilik Eskimos on the Sea Ice,* © 1968, 1969 Education Development Center, Inc., Newton, Mass. Used with permission. This publication is not endorsed by the copyright holder.

2. Cut the remainder of the bucket into blocks and glue them in a spiral, beginning at point X (see illustration A). It is a good idea to cut one block and glue it before cutting another. The first blocks are almost rectangular. Successive blocks become more curved. The glue can fill in cracks, so fitting need not be exact.

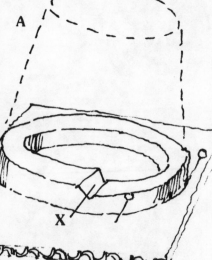

C

3. The last six blocks can be strung on a thread or numbered for fitting. You may eventually want to glue these blocks to the top of the igloo or together to form a removable lid.

The Igloo Game

In the Building Your Own Igloo section, you discovered how Eskimos build their homes. Your construction efforts helped you learn a little about the Eskimo way of life.

You might want to test your new-found skill on the Igloo Game shown here. Your task is to figure out the order of steps in building an igloo.

Checkup
Can you build an igloo following your sequence of cards? Look in the appendix on the page called Building An Igloo Game: Checkup.

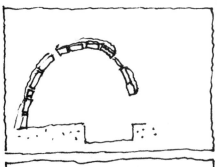

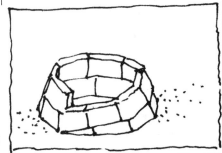

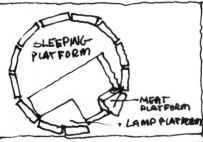

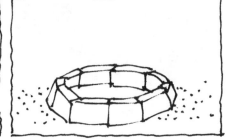

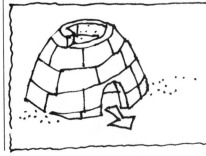

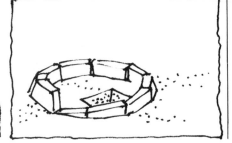

Speaking Without Words

Some people are interested in being able to communicate without words. Can you guess why? If you guessed that two persons or groups of people may not understand each other's words, you're right. In 1960, an astronomer by the name of Frank Drake decided that it was time for humans to listen to broadcasts from extraterrestrial societies, if they were out there. Project OZMA pointed radio telescopes at stars for 2 weeks. The results were negative, but the attempt had been made to communicate without the use of words. Similar attempts continue. Another scientist, John Lilly, headed a project to study how dolphins communicated by recording the sounds they produced.

The work of Peter Fouts proves to be as startling and exciting as that of John Lilly. Fouts has worked with chimpanzees, the most famous being a female named Lucy. He has developed a sign language for the chimpanzees that enables them to communicate with each other. Below is a listing of some of the chimpanzees' vocabulary.

Chimp Communication

1. Refer to the chimpanzees' vocabulary list to determine what word is being communicated in each drawing. Check your answers here: A. string, B. candy/sweet, C. book.

2. Assume that the chimpanzees' list is your entire vocabulary. Get together with a partner. Both of you try to speak to each other without words. One person starts by sending messages to the other person, such as "Kiss me," "Me catch cold," and "Please tickle me." When you feel confident, try making up your own messages and carrying on a conversation for 2 to 5 minutes. Good luck.

The Signs of Silence

Now let's turn our attention to the learning of a sign language. Way before the European settlers' arrival on the shores of North America, North American Indians had languages of their own—over one thousand! Can you imagine having to learn one thousand languages just to be able to talk to people from other tribes? To make this easier, the North American Indians developed a way of communicating called sign language. Now is your chance to acquire this language by learning some of the following signs. You'll need practice as a sender and receiver of sign language messages, each role being equally important for communication. Sit or stand facing a partner. Have one of you practice sending simple messages, while the other receives the message by saying it aloud.

Word	Expression
I	Point to self with thumb.
walk	Hold hands flat, palms down, and make walking motion.
go	Put right hand out pointing down; swing it forward and up.
house	Outline roof of house by joining flat hands in a V.
white man	Move pointing finger across forehead to show brim of hat.
know	Hold hand over heart, thumb and index finger out; move it out and down, turning it so that palm is up.
baby	Both hands held out, palms up; move as if rocking a baby.
sad	Make sign for "good" and drop hand down and out.

Chimpanzees' Early Vocabulary

baby doll	car	dog	hurry	mirror	purse	this/that
ball	cat	drink	hurt	more	run	there
banana	catch	eat	in	no	shoe	tickle
barrette	clean	enough	key	nut	smell	want
berry	cost	flower	kiss	oil	smile	what
blanket	cold	fork	least	open	smoke	yes
blow	comb	fruit	lipstick	out	sorry	you
book	come/gimme	go	listen	pants	spoon	yours
bowl	cry	handkerchief	look	pen/write	string	
brush	cup	hat	me	pipe	swallow	
candy/sweet	dirty	hug	mine	please	telephone	

man	Hold hand pointing up in front of chin.
woman	Pretend to comb hair with curved fingers from top of head to shoulder.
you	Point to the person with index finger.
he, she (him, her)	Point to the person with index finger; if he or she is not there, make sign for "man" or "woman."
all	Starting at right shoulder, move hand, palm down, in a level circle.
we (us)	Make signs for "I" and "all."
question	Use before all questions: hold hand at right shoulder, facing out; bend it to the left and right several times.
why	Make sign for "question" very slowly.
how many	After question, tap spread fingers of left hand with index finger of right; close each finger as it is hit.
stay (sit, here)	Jerk fist down a few inches.
called (named)	Hold a circle, made from thumb and index finger, against mouth; snap mouth open while moving hand forward.
mother	Touch left side of chest several times with hand bunched.
father	Touch right side of chest several times with hand bunched.
heart	Hold bunched hand, pointing down, over heart.
good (all right, fair)	Hold hand flat, palm down, over heart, then move out to the right; this means "evil with the heart."
happy	Make signs for "heart" and "good."

A Little Detective Work: Studying Tools

One of the abilities that humans have in common, no matter where they live, is tool making. The kind of tools made by a group of people clues the anthropologist in to the kind of life they live.

The Netsilik are a tribe of Eskimos who live in the Canadian Arctic near Pelly Bay. They lead a hard life. Their winter begins in September and ends in June. During this time they live on the sea ice, moving onto the land in summer. Their chief sources of food are trout, caribou, and seal.

Here are drawings of six Netsilik Eskimo tools. Apply your powers of observation to figure out what the tools are used for. Write down your ideas next to each tool.

Checkup

How "handy" were you in classifying these tools? Turn to the page in the appendix, A Little Detective Work: Checkup, to see how well you did.

Secret Language Codes

Remember when the note you were passing to your classmate was intercepted by—guess who? If you guessed the bionic-eyed teacher, you're right. Wouldn't you have liked to use a secret code, known only by a few of your friends, especially if you were making comments about the teacher? In this activity you will use three secret language codes and learn how to develop your own.

Try to interpret the following three messages.

Write the messages here.

Message 1._____

Message 2._____

Message 3._____

1
Beep Beeep Beeep
Beep Beep Beep Beep
Beep Beeep
Beeep
Beep Beep
Beep Beep Beep
Beeep Beep Beeep Beeep
Beeep Beeep Beeep
Beep Beep Beeep
Beep Beeep Beep
Beeep Beep
Beep Beeep
Beeep Beeep
Beep
Beep Beep Beeep Beeep Beep Beep

2

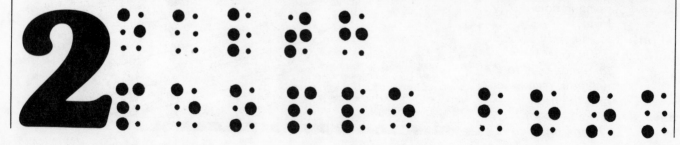

3 □EA△∴ ∪HE ⌐E+△E∪ +O OOE

How did you do? If you didn't do well, don't feel too bad. You've probably guessed that Message 1 is in morse code, but you either don't know morse code or forgot it. Message 2 is in braille, which was invented by Louis Braille, a French teacher of the blind. To find out how blind people read, push through the heavy black dots in Message 2 from the back of the page with a ball point pen. Turn the page back again and feel the bumps with the tips of your fingers. Message 3 is a secret code that was made up for this activity.

Find a book on morse code and braille to check your answers to Messages 1 and 2 and how to learn

these "languages." To learn the secret code, read on!

The Secret Code

This code substitutes symbols for some of the letters in the alphabet. All other letters are unchanged. It is simple, and you can use this format to create your own secret code.

Use the secret code to decode Message 3. You should decode it as "Learn the secret code."

Now that you are able to decode messages from three new languages —one using your sense of sound, the second touch, and the third sight —do you think that there are languages based on smell and taste? Wouldn't this make "sense"?

SECRET CODE

A is A
E is E
I is Y
O is O
U is U

△ is R
□ is L
+ is C
& is N
∞ is D

∪ is T
⌐ is S
⊕ is X
⊔ is H
≡ is Q

All other letters are the same as in the alphabet.

5

The Struggle for Human Rights

Oddly enough, humans have had to struggle with each other to gain human rights. The American Revolution is one example of this struggle.

Colonial men and women revolted against the British Crown because they believed deeply in their own human rights. The Declaration of Independence is the voice of free people demanding their liberty and freedom.

In this chapter you will read about people who fought for their rights. You will also find out about some important events in the struggle for human rights: the earliest experiment with democracy, the Renaissance, and the civil rights movement. You will discover that these struggles can be painful, lonely, and dangerous. Despite these drawbacks, the courage to be free persons and achieve rights for all humans should be a goal for all of us.

governments different? How are they alike?

2. Human thought flourished during the Greek period. Find who these people were and what they contributed to human thought.

Eratosthenes	Euclid	Aristotle
Hippocrates	Homer	Socrates
Archimedes	Herodotus	Pericles
Plato	Sophocles	

An Experiment in Democracy

Answer aye or nay to this true-false question: The United States was the first country to have a democratic form of government. *False. The Greeks were the first democrats!*

Those of us living in the United States forget that our democratic form of government goes back more than two thousand years, not two hundred, to the Greek city-states. The word "democracy" comes from the Greek language and means "rule by the people."

Athens was the most powerful city-state in Greece. The freedom that the people in the democracy enjoyed led to original thinking, profitable business, and advances in art. The political power of the Athenian democracy was held by the assembly, to which all citizens 18 years of age and older belonged. The assembly met out of doors and discussed and voted on major problems. The Athenians also set up a court system, whose citizens' juries decided people's cases.

But not everything about the Greek form of democracy was ideal. Some problems with this early experiment in free government were:

1. The assembly became too large to manage because the Greeks did not use a representative form of democracy as we do.

2. Women and slaves were not granted citizenship.

3. People who settled in Athens were not given the same privileges as those born there.

4. Council and administrative officials were chosen by drawing lots.

Getting to Know the Greeks

1. Compare our form of government to the Athenian democracy. How are the two

Leonardo da Vinci
AND HIS RENAISSANCE FRIENDS

The struggle for freedom is not just a political story. Humans also struggled to become *free thinkers*. The Renaissance was a period in time from about A.D. 1300 to A.D. 1600 that marked the shift from medieval to modern life. We have to go as far back as the Greek and Roman civilizations to catch a glimpse of any intellectual thought before the Renaissance. The Dark Ages—that period in human history just after the fall of Rome in A.D. 476 when thinking, culture, and art were lost—lasted a very, very long time.

Of all the humans of the Renaissance, Leonardo da Vinci stands out as one of the most impressive. He was not only a thinker but a scientist, inventor, and artist. He drew up designs for a flying machine, a girder-supported bridge, a water "alarm clock" device (this device poured water over the sleeper's feet—brrr— much like our modern alarm clock with its ringing bell!), a parachute, and a human-operated flying wing. He also made detailed studies in the areas of water, astronomy, geology, motion of objects, gravity, forces, perpetual motion, percussion, principle of the lever, flight, human anatomy, engineering, and bridge building.

Leonardo never published any of his studies and work, which he kept in notebooks. Our study of these notebooks—the only source of his work—has endowed him with his fame. Look at the notebook sketches on Leonardo's forehead. What do you think these drawings represent? Did you find any of the following?

A. Human heart
B. Parachute
C. Helicopter
D. Artificial wing

The Renaissance brought a return to human culture of individual thinking, science, and art. It marks the beginning of the humanistic movement, a new interest in the beauties and joys of life on earth. Whereas the people of the Middle Ages looked forward to an afterlife, the people of the Renaissance lived for the here-and-now. They created art and culture and used their ingenuity to solve problems. Of all the struggles in human culture, the Renaissance may be one of the most important.

Renaissance Research

1. Find a book on Leonardo da Vinci that contains pictures and drawings of his inventions. Make a list of his inventions and find out how many of his inventions exist today.

2. Find out the names of these people: painter of the Sistine Chapel ceiling, author of The Canterbury Tales, inventor of the printing press.

3. Prepare a folder on any one of the following Renaissance people. Include drawings, copies of papers written by the individual, a brief biography, and a picture of the person.

Cellini	*Cervantes*
Giotto	*Mercator*
Michelangelo	*Pope Gregory XIII*
Gutenburg	*Donatello*
Chaucer	*Dante*
Shakespeare	*Petrarch*

Abraham Lincoln Speaks

FOUR SCORE AND SEVEN YEARS AGO...

Abraham Lincoln was the sixteenth president of the United States. Many persons consider him one of our most important presidents. His ideas won a war, saved the Union, and made a people free.

To see the Lincoln Memorial in Washington, D.C. is to understand the quality of Abe Lincoln. He stood 6 feet 4 inches tall, had a high-pitched voice, and his deep-set eyes flashed and twinkled. When he stood up to speak, his audiences were startled at his phenomenal appearance.

Lincoln did not write any books, and he wrote few letters. He was an orator—a great speaker who brought his ideas to the people through his speeches. Abe Lincoln learned the art of public speaking at the age of fifteen. Often he would mount a stump in an open field to give a speech or make a sermon to his neighborhood playmates. Throughout his career in Congress and as president, he made many speeches. Three of his most famous are:

1. **Farewell Address:** Springfield, Illinois, February 11, 1861. This speech was given the day Lincoln left for Washington, D.C. to become the new president. By this time South Carolina and other states of the deep South had seceded.

2. **Gettysburg Address:** November 19, 1863. After the Battle of Gettysburg, the governors of the Northern states made arrangements for a new cemetery for those who had died in the battle. President Lincoln spoke briefly at the dedication ceremony.

3. **Second Inaugural Address: March 4, 1865.** Lincoln's second inaugural address was the briefest address given by any president. On this inaugural day it was dark and raining in Washington. As soon as he finished his address the sun came out, perhaps as an omen that the clouds of war had blown over.

Enlightening Yourself About Lincoln

1. Look up the text of Lincoln's farewell address. What feelings did he describe?

2. The Civil War split the Union, and President Lincoln worked hard to bring it back together. Find a copy of his second inaugural address and define Lincoln's attitude toward the South.

3. Do some research on any of the following topics. Abraham Lincoln had something to do with each.
   a. Battle of Gettysburg
   b. The Emancipation Proclamation
   c. The Dred Scott Decision
   d. The Lincoln-Douglas

THE COURAGE TO BE FREE: THREE PROFILES

cour•age (kur′ ij) *n*. [Fr. *courage*, L. *cor*, the heart, whence also "cordial," etc.] That quality of mind that enables a person to encounter danger and difficulties with firmness, or without fear; bravery; intrepidity, valor; boldness; resolution.

free•dom (frē′ dom) *n*. [M.E. *fredom*, O.E. *freodom*] The state of being free; exemption from slavery, servitude, or confinement; political liberty; frankness; openness; outspokenness; unrestrictedness; permission; liberality; particular privileges, as the freedom of a city; ease or facility of doing, enjoying, or using something at will.

There are many human beings that we could study to find out about the quality we call courage. Of all the qualities that humans possess, courage is probably the most admired by other humans. Often, the persons who are courageous risk their careers, are unpopular with other people, and, sadly, have their reputations ruined.

We have selected three people from American history who answered the call of their country and of humanity with great courage. John Quincy Adams, Lucretia Mott, and Martin Luther King each displayed courage as their situations demanded. They waved their principles in the face of danger, humiliation, discouragement, and even repeated imprisonment. You will learn that sometimes heroic, courageous people are murdered by those who do not understand.

John Quincy Adams (1767–1848)

John Quincy Adams held more offices and participated in more events than anyone in the history of the United States. He was minister to The Hague, emissary to England, minister to Prussia, state senator, minister to Russia, minister to England, secretary of state, member of the House of Representatives, and president of the United States. He was involved in the American Revolution, the War of 1812, and the rumblings of the Civil War. With all this he once said, "My whole life has been a succession of disappointments. I can scarcely recollect a single instance of success in anything I ever undertook."

John Quincy Adams demonstrated courage by breaking with his political party to fight for the issues that were more important to the nation as a whole. He also antagonized the people who had elected him by speaking out against bills that were in their favor. Why did Adams abandon his state and party in favor of the national interest? Some of the following possibilities suggest themselves. Do you agree with any or all of them?

1. His self-respect was more important than his popularity with others.

2. A reputation for courage was a stronger incentive than reelection to office.

3. His sense of ethics, or morality, was stronger than any pressure of public disapproval.

4. He had faith in the course he was following.

While in the Senate, Adams had supported the purchase of the

From the instant your Slave-holding States become a theater of war… the powers of the Constitution extend to interference with the institution of Slavery in every way that it can be interfered with…

Louisiana Territory by President Jefferson. His own party and the New England states feared the purchase and were very much against it. Still, he supported it and even attended a party to celebrate the purchase. In his journal he wrote that sticking to his principles would cause him problems. People believed that elected officials should follow party policy. Adams felt that he should follow his conscience and do what *he* thought was right. He knew that if he voted against the will of his party, his character and reputation would be smeared. Yet, as he wrote, he decided to make his own choices and accept the consequences. His behavior as a politician was guided by a statement that his father, John Adams, had made years earlier: "The magistrate is the servant not of his own desires, not even of the people, but of his God."

Some Things to Think About

1. John Quincy Adams didn't have many friends because of his courage and determination. Would you give up your friendships to act courageously?

2. What are some principles that guide your behavior? Make a list of them and compare them with other people's lists.

3. In the Congress, senators are elected for 6 year terms and representatives for 2 year terms. How do you think the difference in length of terms might influence the behavior of congresspersons?

Lucretia Mott (1793–1880)

Lucretia Mott was born a Quaker and grew up on the little island of Nantucket in New England. Her father was the captain of a whaler, leaving her mother responsible for her early training. Lucretia would grow up to be a Quaker speaker, one of the most vocal opponents to slavery this country has ever known.

Lucretia opposed slavery even as a young girl. When she was older, she discovered her gift of public speaking. Combining her speaking

ability and antislavery beliefs, she became the chief spokesperson in the country and a pioneer in the movement to abolish slavery.

People soon learned of her beliefs. Sometimes at Quaker religious meetings she was asked not to speak on slavery. One group to whom she spoke said, "We do hope, Mrs. Mott, you will not name slavery, or allude to it this afternoon." "Why," she said, "that is eminently a religious matter. I should consider myself disobedient to the Voice of God in my soul if I did not speak against it."

Lucretia moved quietly to national and world fame. In 1833, a national antislavery society was formed in Philadelphia. She was one of seventy delegates, only four of which were women. In 1834, the Female Antislavery Society, one of the earliest women's groups in this country, was formed and Lucretia Mott was president.

In 1840, she attended the world antislavery convention in London. At this convention women delegates were shut out. She didn't give up. At a tea held before the convention was over she delivered an eloquent speech on slavery.

Lucretia was scorned and laughed at by her friends. Twice, mobs attempted to raid her home. Often groups of men and women threw stones at the windows of the building where she was speaking. Even the Quakers were upset that she sheltered fugitive slaves in her home.

Lucretia lived and believed in nonviolence. Violence could not stop violence, so she sought peaceful means to protest the injustice of slavery. She and her family boycotted all products that involved slave labor.

Lucretia Mott also spoke out for the equal rights of women with men, freedom, and peace.

Thoughts

1. What kind of person do you think Lucretia Mott's husband was?

2. How do you suppose Lucretia Mott's religion influenced her attitude toward slavery?

3. How would you describe Lucretia Mott's courage?

Martin Luther King (1929–1968) . . . "I Have A Dream"

One of Martin Luther King's most famous speeches was his last. It was given in the Masonic Temple in Memphis, Tennessee on April 3, 1968. Dr. King was there to support a group of striking sanitation workers. In the last part of his speech he said

Well I don't know what will happen now. We've got some difficult days ahead. But it doesn't matter with me now. Because I've been to the mountain top. And I don't mind. Like anybody, I would like to have a long life. Longevity has its place. But I'm not concerned about that now. I just want to do God's will. And He's allowed me to go up to the mountain. And I've looked over and I've seen the promised land. I may not get there with you. But I want you to know tonight, that we, as a people will get to the promised land. And I'm happy tonight. I'm not worried about anything. I'm not fearing any man. Mine eyes have seen the glory of the coming of the land.

The day after this speech Martin Luther King was assassinated.

Martin Luther King committed his life to a nonviolent movement that would bring justice to all people in the world, especially black Americans. His peaceful demonstrations, marches, and courage in facing people who were racist and prejudiced were his hallmark. Under his leadership, millions of black Americans emerged from a long intellectual imprisonment, from fear, from apathy, and proclaimed their freedom. He inspired people of all cultural backgrounds to realize their rights,

their dignity, and their power.

In 1964, Martin Luther King was awarded the Nobel Peace Prize, the highest honor a person of nonviolence can aspire to. Peace was not yet a reality, as he pointed out in his acceptance speech, but King accepted the award as a recognition that nonviolence is the answer to violence and oppression of people. Here is part of the text of his Nobel Prize acceptance speech as given on December 10, 1964 in Oslo, Norway.

Your Majesty, your Royal Highness, Mr. President, excellencies, ladies and gentlemen:

I accept the Nobel Prize for Peace at a moment when twenty-two million Negroes of the United States of America are engaged in a creative battle to end the long night of racial injustice. I accept this award in behalf of a civil rights movement which is moving with determination and a majestic scorn for risk and danger to establish a reign of

freedom and a rule of justice.

I am mindful that only yesterday in Birmingham, Alabama, our children, crying out for brotherhood, were answered with fire hoses, snarling dogs and even death. I am mindful that only yesterday in Philadelphia, Mississippi, young people seeking to secure the right to vote were brutalized and murdered.

I am mindful that debilitating and grinding poverty afflicts my people and chains them to the lowest rung of the economic ladder.

Therefore, I must ask why this prize is awarded to a movement which is beleaguered and committed to unrelenting struggle: to a movement which has not won the very peace and brotherhood which is the essence of the Nobel Prize.

What else do you think Martin Luther King said? Complete his speech yourself. Check your ending by looking up the text of his speech in the library.

The Freedom Time Line

History has shown us that freedom's time line is still in progress. At the present time, people from all around the world are speaking out and taking action on human rights.

In this activity, you will make a time line of events and people related to the human struggle for freedom. You'll need about 3 m of adding machine tape or butcher paper, crayons, and the list of events given below. Start your time line at 2000 B.C. and end it at A.D. 2000. Your time line should look something like this.

					Magna Carta	American Revolution
2000 BC	500 BC	0	AD 500	AD 1000	AD 1500	AD 2000

Locate each event in the list on the time line. Search through history books, adding to the events listed here. When you have completed the freedom time line, here are some things to think about and do.

1. What period in human history appears to be the most active in the struggle for human rights?

2. What events do you predict will occur in future struggles for freedom?

List of Events

2000 B.C.	Code of Hammurabi
350 B.C.	Golden Age of Greece
A.D. 476	Fall of Roman Empire
1215	Signing of Magna Carta
1350	Beginning of Renaissance
1500	Protestant Reformation
1776	American and French Revolutions
1862	Emancipation Proclamation
1917	End of World War I
1920	19th Amendment (women's right to vote)
1939	Germany invades Poland
1946	End of World War II
1964	Civil Rights Act
1972	Equal Rights Amendment proposed

Some Things to Do

1. Coretta Scott King, Martin Luther King's wife, has carried on his work and life goals. You can write to her to find out more at the Martin Luther King Jr. Center for Social Change, 671 Beckwith St., Atlanta, GA 30303.

2. This is a list of people who also fought for civil rights. Find out who they were, what they are doing now, and what their contribution to freedom was.

Medgar Evers   Andrew Young
James Meredith   Jessie Jackson
Roy Wilkins   Whitney Young
Ralph Abernathy Rosa Parks
Malcolm X   Stokely Carmichael

3. What were some of Dr. King's concerns about America and the world as outlined in his Nobel Prize acceptance speech?

Projects on Courage and Freedom

1. What happens to you when you do something that you have found to be difficult in the past? Try showing concern for someone you've never cared for. Give someone you don't know very well a sincere compliment. Write how you felt about doing these acts.

2. What is prejudice? Map out the places where you find prejudice and display your map in one of these places. Make a map of the places where you feel prejudice toward something or someone.

3. List all your behaviors that you think are OK but that others think are bad. Who thinks that they are bad? Does this influence your behavior? Have you done something that you thought was right but that others thought was stupid or wrong? Tell about your feelings.

4. Using art paper, paint, and crayons, design your own coat of arms. Here is your chance to communicate visually some of your strong beliefs.

Anne Waldrop's Civil Rights

During the presidential election of 1876, a young woman decided that she had the right to vote. According to governmental officials, Anne Waldrop had acted illegally and was brought to trial. She had been prepared to bring in many witnesses, women friends, and members of the local women's rights league; however, Judge Dauber excluded everyone but the persons involved directly in the case from the courtroom. His court would not be a soapbox for every Jane, Ann, and Mary. After a day and a half of testimony, Miss Waldrop was brought before Judge Dauber for sentencing.

The following is the account of the end of the trial. Use the information as the basis for a play. Set up a room with props to look like a courtroom.

Judge Dauber: *The court orders the prisoner to stand up and come before the bench to hear the decision of the jury. Before pronouncing the decision of the court, have you, Miss Waldrop, anything to say as to why this* sentence should not be pronounced?

Miss Waldrop: *Yes, I have, Your Honor. While there are many things I would like to say, I would like to emphasize only those that are most important, for in this court you have already trampled every vital principle and civil right of our government. The sentence that you are about to read is a court-ordered verdict of guilty. My rights, whether they be my natural rights, my political rights, my civil rights, or my judicial rights, have all been refused me and ignored by this court. I have been robbed of all my fundamental privileges and rights of citizenship in this, the land of the free. I have been degraded from the status of a citizen to that of a subject. Even worse, all of my sex will be, by Your Honor's decision, doomed to political and legalized subjugation under this so-called democratic government.*

Judge Dauber: *This court will not stand by and listen to the defendant restate the same arguments presented by the defendant's counsel earlier this morning. The court especially wants to remind the defendant that* her arguments consumed nearly three hours of the court's time, ample opportunity to include any meaningful and useful arguments to support the defendant's case. Such repetition is not appropriate now.

Miss Waldrop: *May it please Your Honor, I do not wish to argue the question. I am simply trying to state the reasons why this guilty sentence cannot and should not, in justice, be pronounced against me. By denying me my legitimate right as a citizen of this nation to vote for the administrators of the government, you have denied me my right of consent as one of the governed, my right of representation as one of the taxed, and my right to a trial by jury of my peers as an offender against law. But most of all, your denial of my citizen's right to vote is a denial of my sacred and natural rights of life, liberty, property, and . . .*

Judge Dauber: *The court will not and cannot allow the prisoner to go on!*

Miss Waldrop: *So! Your Honor persists in denying me my rights! Will you also deny me this one and single privilege of protest and* speech against this single-handed attack upon my citizen's rights? Now you have taken away my rights and want to refuse me any privileges that I at least thought, maybe mistakenly, that I had some access to as a person living in this country. May it please the court to remember that since the day of my arrest last November, this is the very first time that either I or any person of my sex has been allowed a word of defense before judge or jury. I am dismayed that . . .

Judge Dauber (Rapping the bench with his gavel): *The court cannot allow this behavior! The prisoner must sit down immediately!*

Miss Waldrop: *My prosecutors, every one of them, from the third-ward drug store politician who entered the complaint, to the federal marshal, the commissioner, the district attorney, the district judge—even Your Honor on the bench—not one of them is my peer; but each and all are my political sovereigns. As if this were not bad enough, had Your Honor submitted my case to the jury, as was clearly your duty, I would still have had just cause to protest, for not one of those men was my peer. Each and every man, native or foreign born, white or black or red, rich or poor, educated or ignorant, sober or drunk, awake or asleep, informed or uninformed, healthy or ill, employed or unemployed, is my political and legal superior.*

Judge Dauber: *The court must order the prisoner to cease this disturbance. Miss Waldrop, you are running the risk of being charged with contempt. The prisoner has been tried according to the established procedures of law and justice in this land.*

Miss Waldrop: *Yes, you're right, Your Honor. I have been tried according to the established procedures of law and justice, but may I again remind the court, and Your Honor, that these procedures, the law, and the form of justice were all devised by men, interpreted by men, administered by men, in favor of men, and enforced against women. Thus, Your Honor's prepared verdict of guilty is based solely on the premise that a woman, not a man,*

exercised the citizen's right to vote in a political election. However, only yesterday the same manmade forms of law and justice declared it a criminal act, punishable by both fine and imprisonment, for men and women—for you, Your Honor, and for me or any of us—to give a cup of cold water, a crust of bread, or a night's shelter to a panting fugitive as he attempted to reach Canada. And you and I both know, and it is now a matter of public record, that every man, woman, and child that possessed even the faintest drop of human sympathy violated that law. . . . I am a woman and I will not suffer just because I am a woman!*

Judge Dauber: *The court will not allow the prisoner to continue! It has heard more than enough of this protest! The court orders the prisoner to sit down immediately!*

Miss Waldrop (Refusing to sit down): *When it was announced that I would be brought to this particular court and that my trial was to be heard before Your Honor, I had high hopes that the Constitution and its recent amendments would be interpreted broadly and liberally and that this court would see that the rights of all citizens are theirs regardless of sex. I had hopes that this court would declare all citizens of these United States under its protective*

aegis. I had hoped that this court would declare that civil and political rights were extended to all citizens and that the courts were to protect and guarantee these rights equally to all citizens. What I had hoped for is not to be fulfilled. I have failed to receive real justice, the justice guaranteed me and all citizens under the Constitution. I have failed even to receive a trial by jury that included men and women, both of whom are my peers. Since I have failed, I do not ask the court for leniency or forgiveness; rather, I ask the court to deal with me with the full rigor of the law and of justice.*

Judge Dauber: *Miss Waldrop, I must insist that you . . .* (Prisoner now sits down. A few seconds pass to allow the courtroom to settle down.) *The court orders the prisoner to stand up to hear the verdict of the jury.* (**Miss Waldrop** slowly stands, her face revealing no emotion.) *The court finds the prisoner guilty as charged. The sentence of the court is that the prisoner pay the required fine of $150 and the costs of the prosecution.*

Civil (and Uncivil) Thoughts

1. What law did Anne Waldrop break?

2. If you were Miss Waldrop, which of the following actions would you follow?

   a. Pay the $150 fine and the court costs.

   b. Refuse to pay the fine and court costs to find out what action the court would take.

   c. Pay the fine but make a public statement commiting yourself to fight for the civil rights of women.

3. When did women get the right to vote in the United States? Find out about some of the women and men who worked hard for this right.

4. Are there women active in the women's movement who remind you of Anne Waldrop?

From J. Doyle Casteel and Robert J. Stahl, *Value Clarification in the Classroom: A Primer* (Santa Monica, Calif.: Goodyear Publishing, 1975), pp. 45–46. Used with permission.

A Children's Bill of Rights

Childhood is a stage in life that we all pass through. Our parents at home and teachers at school oversee our childhood. Home and school take up most of a child's time. As children grow up they are told that one day in the future they will be able to do the things that adults do: voting, choosing an education and a career, and so forth.

What rights do children between 1 and 18 years of age have as they pass through childhood?* Below is a set of rights for children. Some of these may be quite controversial, while others may not. Read them.

Children's Bill of Rights

Article 1. Each child has the right to equal treatment at the hands of the law. This would apply in any situation, including home and school.

Article 2. Each child has the right to vote and take full part in local, state, and national political affairs.

Article 3. Each child has the right to work and earn money.

Article 4. Each child has the right to control and choose an education.

Article 5. Each child has the right to travel, to live away from home, and to rent or build a place to live.

Article 6. Each child has the right to own, buy, or sell property; borrow money; establish credit; and sign contracts.

Article 7. Each child has the right to receive from the government whatever minimum income is guaranteed to adult citizens.

Article 8. Each child has the right to free speech, assembly, and petition.

Article 9. Each child has the right to privacy.

Article 10. Each child has the right to relationships outside the immediate family.

Article 11. Each child has the right to do what any adult may legally do.

Adapted from John Holt, *Escape From Childhood* (New York: Ballantine Books, 1974).

Now that you have read them, perhaps you would like to do one or more of the following exercises:

1. Conduct a survey of children and adults on each right. Do adults feel differently than children about children's rights?

2. Check off those rights that you think are important. Then do research to define in detail what each right entails. When you have completed your research, prepare copies for your senator and congressperson. Ask their opinion and suggestions for getting rights for children.

3. How does the Children's Bill of Rights compare to the Bill of Rights of our Constitution?

4. How do you think the Children's Bill of Rights listed here would affect your life at home, in school, and in general?

5. Debate the rights listed here with a group of people. Be sure to include both children and adults.

6. Use the list as a petition. Obtain as many signatures as you can and present it to your local government for action.

7. Rewrite each right the way you think it should be stated.

*Eighteen years may not be the age at which childhood ends. Sixteen-year-olds can marry in some states, drive a car in nearly all states, and hold a job. In most situations, however, we are not considered adults until age 18.

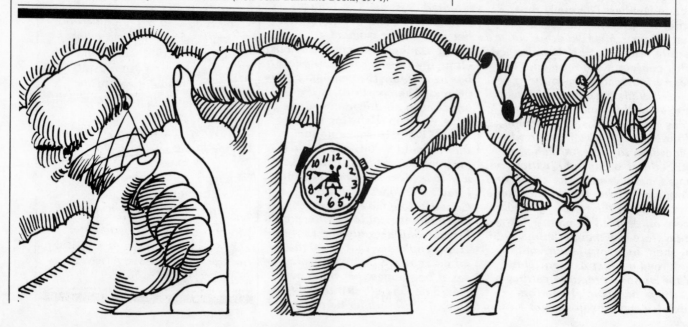

The Right to a Public Education

Many people in the United States who go to college go to a public-supported college or university. The state that you live in probably has many state colleges, junior colleges, and one or two universities. State-supported universities make it possible for most citizens to obtain a quality education.

There have been many problems in our country related to education. These include

1. Integration of schools
2. Busing of elementary and secondary school students to carry out court-ordered integration
3. Removal of prayer from public schools
4. Strikes by teachers in many school systems
5. Parental refusal to send children to school because of busing or integration
6. The open or free school movement
7. Reports and books about the failure of our schools to help students learn

One problem we have faced in this country is equal educational opportunity for people from minority groups. As late as 1962, blacks were forced to attend segregated schools in Alabama, Mississippi, and South Carolina. One of the most controversial cases of a black person's struggle to obtain an education of his own choice was that of James Meredith.

In 1962, James Meredith applied for admission to the University of Mississippi but was not admitted. On September 10, 1962, Justice Black of the United Sates Supreme Court ordered that James Meredith be admitted to the University. However, the governor of Mississippi, Ross Barnett, then ruled that all public schools and universities operated under state officials and obeyed laws passed by the state legislature. Blacks were not allowed in white schools, and the governor personally blocked Mr. Meredith at the doorway.

But James Meredith did not give up. He felt that he had the same right to an education at a public university as any white citizen. On his next attempt at admission—his fourth—he was joined by two U.S. marshals. This time he was greeted by the Mississippi state police and a large mob. Meredith decided not to register that day.

At this point, President John Kennedy and Attorney-General Robert Kennedy decided to enter the case. They spoke with Governor Barnett to get him to change his mind about James Meredith. The Governor changed his mind—after Kennedy ordered federal troops to the campus to enforce Supreme Court Justice Black's decision. Meredith was admitted to the University of Mississippi and received his degree on August 18, 1963. His long and difficult struggle for admission made it possible for other blacks to obtain an education at the school of their choice.

Some "Admissions"

1. What would you have done in this case if you had been James Meredith?

2. Should federal troops enforce laws?

3. After James Meredith enrolled as a student, he said that his days were lonely because white students refused to recognize him. Have you ever been that lonely? How did it feel? What did you do about it?

4. Have you ever been prevented from having something you thought you had the right to have? What were the circumstances? What did you do to try to get what you wanted?

5. Four years after James Meredith was admitted to the University of Mississippi, he was shot by a sniper. This occurred while he was on a peaceful march through that state. He had gone with a handful of friends to see the progress of Mississippi and to challenge his own courage. What are some of your feelings about James Meredith's courage?

6

Heroes, Heroines, and Rascals

Each person in this chapter has done something to affect our world in some way. Most of them are he-roes or her-oines, but some are rascals, and you may not approve of what they've done, written, or said.

You may have heard of some people in this chapter. Most of them will be unknown to you. History books don't pay much attention to them and Hollywood producers don't make films about their lives. You won't find George

Washington in these pages. You won't even find Abraham Lincoln. Clara Barton isn't here, and neither is Booker T. Washington. Well, then, who is here? May we introduce our he-roes, her-oines, and rascals. . . .

Phyllis Wheatley-A Young Black Poet

(1753–1784)

Phyllis Wheatley was only 8 years old when she was brought to America as a slave. This young black girl was sick, starving, and probably terrified as she left the slave ship in Boston Harbor. She was bought by John Wheatley, a Boston merchant, who was shopping for a young slave to serve as a maid for his wife.

In many ways, Phyllis was probably one of the few slaves to have a good life after being brought to America. The Wheatley family was very kind to her and taught her many things. She learned English very rapidly and was able to read very difficult parts of the Bible within a few years of her arrival in America. The Wheatleys taught her history, Latin, and writing. By the age of 13 she had started to write poetry. That poetry would eventually lead her to fame.

Phyllis Wheatley wrote a poem dedicated to George Washington

that included these lines:

Thee first in peace and humor, we demand

The grace and glory of thy martial band,

Famed for thy valor, for thy virtues more,

Hear every tongue, thy guardian aid implore!

Washington received this poem in December 1775. He wrote a

thank-you letter to Phyllis Wheatley on February 28, 1776.

Although she was becoming very well known, Phyllis began to have some serious trouble. All the members of the Wheatley family died within a short period of time, and the family business collapsed. Phyllis Wheatley remained, a very poor young woman, sick and in debt. She earned a little money teaching and became the wife of John Peters. Her life ended sadly. Peters did not like to work and she had to sell her possessions to buy fuel. She died in 1784 at the age of 31.

Wondering About Wheatley

1. If you had been Phyllis Wheatley, how would you have felt upon leaving the slave ship?

2. Do you think that many African slaves had the opportunities that Phyllis Wheatley had?

3. Phyllis Wheatley did eventually visit with George Washington. If you had been she, what would you have wanted to talk about with Washington?

Female Freedom Fighters

During the American Revolution, various women did some very courageous things to help in the fight for freedom. **Sybil Ludington** rode horseback for 40 miles on April 26, 1777 to tell the defenders of Danbury, Connecticut that the British troops were going to attack the city. She was 16 years old at the time. **Nancy Hart** captured five British soldiers and held them at gunpoint until American soldiers arrived. **Grace and Rachel Martin** captured two British officers and a courier and sent the military papers that they were carrying to the American General, Nathaniel Greene. Some women actually fought in the Revolutionary War, including **Mary Hays,** who fought at the Battle of Monmouth, and **Margaret Corbin,** who was wounded at Fort Washington in 1776.

One woman disguised herself as a man and fought as a soldier in the American Revolution. Her name was **Deborah Sampson.** She married after the war, so she is also known as Deborah Gannett. This Massachusetts woman dressed herself in men's clothing and enlisted in the army under the name Robert Shurtleft. Wounded during a small battle near Tarrytown, New York, she treated her own wounds so that doctors would not discover that she was a woman. In October 1783, she became very ill and was taken to a hospital, where the medical staff discovered she was a woman. She left the army in October 1783.

War and Women

1. Do you think that women should be allowed to fight in wars? Why or why not?
2. Visit the armed services

recruiters for your city or town. They will probably have offices in a federal building. Pick up some brochures and pamphlets that describe the job opportunities, pay, and other benefits for women in the armed forces.

Nat Turner
(1800-1831)

Slavery existed in the United States until the end of the Civil War. During the long history of slavery, various black men and women tried to snap their chains by physically overthrowing their masters and doing violence. One of the best-known leaders of a slave revolt was Nat Turner, a slave in Virginia. He was a religious man who felt that he had been appointed by God to help slaves break free of their masters.

Nat Turner organized slaves in Southampton County, Virginia and within two days had a force of sixty armed men. His small army attacked the houses of white slave holders and killed over fifty white people. Nat Turner and his followers decided to attack the county seat at Jerusalem, Virginia

and began to move toward it. On the way, a posse of law enforcement officers and citizens caught up with them. The small army was scattered. Turner managed to escape the posse and hid out in a large swampy area for about 6 weeks. Nat Turner and sixteen other black men were eventually captured, brought to trial, and

sentenced to death by hanging.

Tune in to Nat Turner
1. If you had been a slave during Nat Turner's time, would you have joined his revolt? Why or why not?
2. Do you think Nat Turner's punishment fit his "crimes"? Why or why not?

Heroines in the Struggle for the Right to Vote

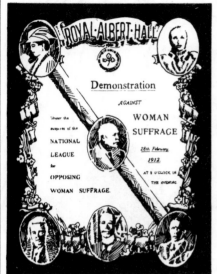

Women around the world go to the polls to cast their votes. Many people may not realize that this simple act is the result of a long and hard struggle. Before laws were passed giving women the right to vote, many men (and women) felt that women should not be involved in decisions about government. To them, a woman's place was in the home. Until the early part of this century, the male 50 percent of the population—brothers, fathers, and husbands—made all the decisions that affected 100 percent of the population.

Suffragettes were women who believed in their right to vote. They spoke their views, gathered signatures on petitions, held rallies and marches, and some were even sent to prison. Here are some drawings of posters about suffragettism from Great Britain that show the variety of opinions that people held in the early 1900s.
Suffering Suffragettes!
1. What does the expression "My umbrella protects us all!" mean on the poster that has John Bull on it? (John Bull is the English term for the typical

These drawings are based on posters that appeared in the early part of this century in England.

English man. We would use John Doe.)
2. Why does the woman on the John Bull poster want her own umbrella?
3. Which one of the drawings is definitely against women's right to vote? There is a picture on it of a woman who was antisuffragette. Why do you think that she felt this way?
4. Is the third poster for or against women's suffrage? How well does it get its message across?

Emmeline Pankhurst
(1858–1928)

The leader in the struggle for women's voting rights in England was Emmeline Pankhurst. Her husband died in 1898, leaving her with four children to raise and very little money. From this very shaky position she rose to become a lifelong activist for women's rights. In 1903 she started the Women's Social and Political Union, which

tried to convince the British Parliament of women's right to vote.

The WSPU did many things to attract people to its cause. Its members flew across London in a hot-air balloon to drop leaflets, presented a petition to King Edward VII, and even chained themselves to the fences outside the prime minister's residence.

At various times, members of the

WSPU were sent to jail for their actions. Christabel Pankhurst, one of Emmeline's daughters, was arrested and sent to prison for creating a disturbance in 1905. She was released a short time later. In 1908 Emmeline and Christabel Pankhurst were both arrested and charged with "a breach of the peace." They were found guilty and sent to prison for creating a disturbance at a rally in Trafalgar Square. After their release from prison, they continued their activities. In 1913 Emmeline Pankhurst was again sent to jail, this

Susan Brownell Anthony
(1820–1906)

The true republic—men, their rights and nothing more; women, their rights and nothing less.

time for three years, because of a violent demonstration by the WSPU. She was soon released, however, after she went on a hunger strike. The authorities were worried that she would die in jail. After her release, she and her daughters Christabel and Sylvia carried on with their work. World War I intervened, and many women became involved in the war effort.

In 1918, after the war, the Representation of the People Act was passed. It bestowed the right to vote upon women as well as upon some men who had not been allowed to vote, poor men, for example. According to this law, women could not vote until they were 30, although men could vote at age 21. In 1928 the voting age for women became the same as that for men. This same year Emmeline Pankhurst died.

Some Things to Ponder
1. Have women organized recently to get laws passed? What were the laws about?

2. Emmeline Pankhurst was sent to jail a number of times for her role in the fight for women's rights. If you had been she, would you have resisted going to jail for your ideas?

The most well-known person involved in American women's struggle to obtain the right to vote was Susan B. Anthony. She was born to Quaker parents in Adams, Massachusetts. As a young woman she taught school in rural New York State. It was customary in those days for teachers to live with the families of the children they taught. As she moved about the countryside she became aware of the hardships and lack of privileges that women had.

In 1868, she and Elizabeth Stanton wrote and published a weekly newspaper, *The Revolution,* that called for increased women's rights. She tried to vote in 1872 and was arrested, found guilty of "illegal voting," and fined $100. She was set free but never paid the fine. In 1892 she was elected president of the National American Woman Suffrage Association.

Susan B. Anthony, a hardy crusader for women's right to vote, never lived to see it happen. She died in Rochester, New York in 1906. Fourteen years later the Nineteenth Amendment was added to the United States Constitution.

The following forty-one words

represent what Susan B. Anthony and thousands of other women had worked so hard for.

Article XIX
The right of the citizens of the United States to vote shall not be denied or abridged by the United States or by any State on account of sex.

Congress shall have the power to enforce this Article by appropriate legislation.

Amending Your Thoughts
1. Do you think that the religious beliefs of Susan B. Anthony's parents influenced her thinking about the rights of people?

2. If Susan B. Anthony were alive today, what kinds of things would she be involved in? Do you think she would be in the women's movement?

3. What would life be like today if the Nineteenth Amendment hadn't been approved? In your opinion, has the right to vote had much effect on U.S. politics and government?

Chief Joseph

Chief Joseph was a leader of the Nez Percé Indians. An 1855 treaty had given this tribe of North American Indians the right to keep their land in the Northwest of the United States. The white prospectors who discovered gold on Nez Percé land ignored this right. By 1875, white settlers determined to have all the Nez Percé land.

In 1877 Chief Joseph was told to move his people off the land. He began to organize his people for the move. For reasons that are still not clear the army attacked his tribe. Knowing that his people could not possibly win against the U.S. army, he decided to retreat to Canada. The army chased him and his followers for a thousand miles and stopped him before he was able to get his people across the Canadian border. The soldiers outnumbered his people by two to one.

Chief Joseph had vainly tried to keep his land and save his people. The words of his surrender were **Tell General Howard I know his heart. What he told me before, I have in my heart. I am tired of fighting. Our chiefs are killed. The old are all dead. . . . It is cold and we have no blankets, the little children are freezing to death. . . . I am tired, my heart is sick and sad. From where the sun now stands, I will fight no more forever.**

If You're Interested in Indians
1. The North American Indians were here long before the Whites, so why did white people feel that they had a right to Indian lands?
2. Do you think that movies about the Wild West depict North American Indians fairly? Why do you feel the way you do?

Cesar Chavez

This Mexican-American was born near Yuma, Arizona in 1927. He was one of five children of a poor farm family. By the time Cesar was 10 years old his father was unable to keep the small family farm going, so the Chavez family left the farm and became migrant workers. They worked as fruit and vegetable pickers in various places in the Southwest. The work was hard, the hours long, and the wages low.

In 1952, while working in the orchards in San José, California, Cesar Chavez became involved with the Community Service Organization to help Mexicans become U.S. citizens. In 1958, as its leader, he began to think about organizing all Mexican-American migrant workers.

Cesar Chavez started a union in 1962. It had less than three hundred members and was called the National Farm Workers' Association (NFWA). By 1965, its members had increased by two thousand Mexican-American migrant worker families. The union worked hard to get crop growers to provide higher wages and better living conditions.

The NFWA also tried to effect a contract with the growers so that the improvement in pay and conditions would last.

Chavez had no success in getting a contract and in 1965 his union began a strike, refusing to pick fruit. The strike, or, in Spanish, La Huelga, received a lot of press coverage across the country. People in many parts of the United States refused to buy grapes from growers who had not signed a contract with Chavez's union. Violence occurred in the fields when growers hired nonunion members to pick the grapes. The struggle between Chavez's union and the grape growers went on.

In April 1970, the first contract with grape growers in California was signed. Three important parts of the contract were that

1. The pay for workers who had been earning about $1.65 an hour plus 25c per box of grapes picked was raised 10c an hour.

2. The union was to receive 12c from the growers for each box of grapes. This money was to be used to help workers with medical care and other necessities.

3. The growers agreed to stop using DDT in the fields.

This contract was the first of many important changes in the lives of migrant workers. Cesar Chavez is still working hard to improve the lives of the migrant workers in the Southwest. He is a man from a poor family who has devoted his life to helping others.

"Belaboring" Some Points

1. If you were a grape grower, what would be your opinion of Chavez and his union? Why would you feel the way you do?

2. When people refuse to buy a product, they *boycott* the product. The boycott is a powerful tool used by labor to force farmers or businesses to accede to its demands. Interview ten people to find out if they were ever part of a boycott. Find out what they refused to buy and why they refused to buy it.

Hiram Fong

Hiram Fong was born and raised in Hawaii. His parents were very poor and he worked on sugar cane plantations to help support his family. When a student, he was also a newsboy, shoeshine boy, and caddy, yet he earned good grades in school. He did not have enough money to go directly to college, so he worked for 3 years at the Pearl Harbor Naval Shipyard.

Later on, he graduated as an honor student from the University of Hawaii—in just 3 years. He went to Harvard Law School and then returned to Hawaii, where he established the law firm of Fong, Miho, Choy, and Robinson. At this time he became active in Hawaiian political life. In July 1959, he became the first U.S. senator from Hawaii.

Hiram Fong's lifelong conviction was that if men and women of different races could learn to work together, they would achieve world peace. Among the many honors he received for his hard work toward this cause was the National Award for Oustanding Service to Brotherhood, given to him by the National Conference of Christians and Jews.

Shirley Chisholm

This very influential black woman was born to a poor family in Brooklyn, New York. Her father was a laborer in a burlap bag factory and her mother worked as a domestic. Although as a young girl Shirley Chisholm left Brooklyn to live with her grandmother in Barbados, she returned to Brooklyn when she was 11 years old.

An excellent student in school, Shirley had scholarship offers from various colleges. She selected Brooklyn College and received her bachelor of arts degree in sociology with a minor in Spanish. A few years after her graduation from Brooklyn College, she earned a master of arts degree in elementary school teaching from Columbia.

In 1954 she became the director of a child care center in Manhattan.

Her work with poor children and their parents awoke her interest in what government was doing for the underprivileged. Her election to the New York State Assembly in 1964 made her the first black woman to be elected to a state assembly. In 1968 she ran for Congress. The fifth of November saw Shirley Chisholm become the first black woman ever elected to the U.S. Congress.

Over the years Shirley Chisholm has worked for laws that will raise the living standards of poor people of all races. She has received many awards for her work and continues to be a very outspoken woman on equal opportunity for jobs, education, and health care.

Chisholm, Continued
1. If you were elected to the House of Representatives, what are three laws that you would try to get passed?
2. Do you think that the United States will ever have a black woman president? What problems would a black woman have to overcome in order to win an election for the presidency?

IeohMingPei

This son of a well-to-do banker was born in Canton, China. His family always stressed the importance of getting a good education and working hard. Ieoh Ming Pei was an excellent student all through elementary and high school. He came to the United States to study architecture and graduated from the Massachusetts Institute of Technology in 1939.

America is his new homeland, and Pei has contributed much to America in the field of architecture. Among the many buildings that he has designed are the Everson Museum of Art in Syracuse, New York; the National Center for Atmospheric Research in Boulder, Colorado; Kips Bay Plaza, an apartment development in New York City; and the skyscraper at Place Ville-Marie in Montreal. Following the assassination of John F. Kennedy, the President's family and a group of architects selected Pei to design a memorial. The John F. Kennedy Memorial Library at Harvard University is a beautiful tribute to the slain president and the genius of I. M. Pei.

Reies Lopes Tijerina
(RAY-es LO-pez Tee-hair-EEN-ah)

Reies Tijerina was born in a South Texas cotton field in 1926. His mother had been picking cotton in the field and returned to work after his birth. The Tijerina family worked hard for poor wages on land owned by others.

After Reies' mother died, the Tijerinas became migrant farm workers, traveling to pick crops as they ripened in other people's fields. They went as far as Michigan to harvest beets. The children of migrant workers received very little schooling because they were always on the move. Reies Tijerina first went to school when he was 11 and he entered the second grade.

As he grew older, he decided that as a preacher he could fight for the rights of poor people. Reies Tijerina traveled throughout the Southwest to preach about justice and the rights of farm workers. After a year he decided to take some action and began to organize poor Mexican-Americans to protest the rights of white landowners to their land.

Reies Tijerina and his followers feel that the U.S. government has broken the Treaty of Guadalupe Hidalgo, an agreement signed in 1848 at the end of the Mexican-American War. The U.S. government broke the treaty when it gave the land to white Americans. Tijerina believes that the Mexicans who originally had the land should get to keep it.

Tijerina has organized Alianza in an attempt to recover the land. The thousands of members of Alianza have sometimes used violent means. In June 1967, twelve thousand soldiers and police were sent to Tierra Amanilla in the state of New Mexico to stop Alianza from taking over the town. Various members of the group including Tijerina were arrested and brought to trial. During the trial Tijerina told the jury:

Yes, we are guilty of wanting our lands. We are guilty of believing in the Treaty of Guadalupe Hidalgo. . . . If I deserve to be punished for what I am doing for the poor people, then do it. But you cannot get rid of the land problems by putting Tijerina in jail.

The jury decided that he was innocent of the charges. Since then, Tijerina and members of the Alianza have continued their protests. Tijerina has been sent to jail many times but he continues to lead Mexican-Americans who are struggling for their rights in the American Southwest.

Reflecting on Rights

1. Name some other leaders of minority groups who have led protest movements in this century. Do they have anything in common with Reies Tijerina?

2. People who believe that their rights have been taken away sometimes react violently. Do you feel that violence solves problems or causes more problems?

BettyFriedan
(1921–   )

Much of the recent interest in getting equal rights for women may be traced to Betty Friedan. The various organizations for women and the increased numbers of women in government and industry are the results of her work back in the 1960s. Her best-selling book, The Feminine Mystique, focused the attention of many people on the problems of modern women.

Betty Friedan took her ideas from print to practical application when she organized the National Organization for Women. One of the main goals of NOW is to end job discrimination against women.

Betty Friedan was born in Peoria, Illinois and attended school in the Midwest. She moved to the East Coast to attend Smith College, where she majored in psychology but spent a great deal of her free time editing a literary magazine and writing articles.

Her ability to write, organize her thoughts, and express herself as a public speaker has helped her greatly in the struggle for women's rights.

Does Equal *Mean* Equal?

1. Many people feel that women already have the same rights and opportunities as men. Do you agree or disagree?

2. Are there any jobs in our society that you feel women should definitely not hold? Why do you feel the way you do?

3. Should there be a men's rights movement?

4. Are there any jobs in our society that men should definitely not hold?

Reading About Heroes, Heroines, and Rascals

Asia Who's Who. Hong Kong: Pan Asia Newspaper Alliance, 1960.

Brownmiller, Susan. Shirley Chisholm. New York: Pocket Books, 1972.

Center for American Women and Politics. Women in Public Office. New York: R. R. Bowker, 1976.

Chisholm, Shirley. Unbought and Unbossed. Boston: Houghton Mifflin, 1970.

Clarke, John Henrik, ed. Malcolm X: The Man and His Times. New York: Macmillan, 1969.

Dobler, Lavinia, and Toppin, Edgar A. Pioneers and Patriots. Garden City, N.Y.: Doubleday, 1965.

Eggenberger, David I., ed. Encyclopedia of World Biography. New York: Macmillan, 1973.

Haber, Louis. Black Pioneers of Science and Invention. New York: Harcourt Brace Jovanovich, 1970.

Keene, Henry George. An Oriental Biographical Dictionary. Danna Bhawan, Delhi: Manohar Reprints, 1971.

Lutz, Alma. Susan B. Anthony: Rebel, Crusader, Humanitarian. Boston: Beacon Press, 1959.

Metcalf, George. Black Profiles, rev. ed. Highstown, N.J.: McGraw-Hill, 1970.

Moritz, Charles, ed. Current Biography. Bronx, N.Y.: H. W. Wilson. Published monthly.

Oates, Stephen B. The Fires of Jubilee: Nat Turner's Fierce Rebellion. New York: Harper & Row, 1975.

Rogers, J. A. World's Great Men of Color. New York: Macmillan, 1972.

Rosenblum, Morris. Heroes of Mexico. New York: Fleet Press, 1969.

Santa Barbara County Board of Education. Emerging Minorities in America. Santa Barbara, Calif.: Clio Press, 1972.

Smith, Margaret Chase, and Jeffers, H. Paul. Gallant Women. Highstown, N.J.: McGraw-Hill, 1968.

Steiner, Stan. La Raza: The Mexican Americans. New York: Harper & Row, 1969.

Sterling, Philip. Sea and Earth: The Life of Rachel Carson. New York: Dell Books, 1970.

Toppin, Edgar A. A Biographical History of Blacks in America. New York: David McKay, 1971.

Tragle, Henry Irving. The Southhampton Slave Revolt of 1831. Amherst, Mass.: University of Massachusetts Press, 1971.

Tuck, Jay Nelson, and Vergara, Norma C. Heroes of Puerto Rico. New York: Fleet Press, 1969.

Who's Who of American Women. Chicago: Marquis Who's Who, Inc., 1972.

Who's Who Among Black Americans. Northbrook, Ill.: Who's Who Among Black Americans, Inc., 1976.

Who's Who in Canada. Toronto: International Press, 1975.

Who's Who in Government. Chicago: Marquis Who's Who, Inc., 1975.

Who's Who in the United Nations. New York: Arno Press, 1975.

Gloria Steinem

The movement for equal rights for women owes much to Gloria Steinem. She is well known as a writer, lecturer, television personality, and one of the founders of *Ms.* magazine.

Ms. Steinem was raised in a poor environment and received poor grades in school. Nevertheless, Smith College accepted her because of her high entrance examination scores. At Smith she emerged as an excellent student, won scholarships, and graduated magna cum laude with a major in government.

After her graduation she went to India to study at universities in Delhi and Calcutta. A few years later she decided to become a writer and came to New York City. Her articles appeared in *Vogue, Glamour, McCall's, Ladies Home Journal, Life,* and *Cosmopolitan* magazines.

During the late 1960s she actively supported candidates for equal rights of minority groups. The 1970s found her at work with people like Betty Friedan, Shirley Chisholm, and Bella Abzug to call attention to the needs of women and minority group members. With these women and many others, Gloria Steinem has organized groups such as the National Women's Political Caucus and the Women's Action Alliance.

What About Women?

1. Some people feel that the women's movement is a threat to our society. What do you think about this?

2. Interview men and women and find out their views on the following statements:

a. A woman's place is in the home.

b. Girls and boys should be raised alike.

c. Women should not do hard physical labor.

7

History/Herstory: YOURstory!

History/herstory bores some people, people who feel that it is a dull collection of facts, names, and places. These unfortunates have missed out on the most enjoyable part of history/herstory—tracking it down. And that makes it yourstory!

Historians use detective-like methods to explore the past. Clues from the past help them understand why people thought and acted the way they did. Historians study old newspapers, pictures, and objects. They interview senior citizens.

In this chapter you'll be doing a historian's detective work to understand the past. Your knowledge of the past will also reveal to you your community, your own family history, and yourself.

People

PICTURE HISTORY

Ask your parents for permission to look through old and new photographs. Try to find pictures of grand-parents, great-grandparents, parents, brothers, sisters, and, of course, YOURSELF.

It's important to preserve these valuable photos. Use a copying machine to make duplicates and return the original pictures to your family scrapbook. You can use the copies for your detective work without endangering the originals.

Arrange your copies from the oldest to the most recent. Paste the copies on individual sheets of paper, leaving room at the bottom for your detective notes.

Study the pictures and jot down some notes. Ask your parents and other relatives for help. It's not easy being a historical detective, so don't feel bad if you can't dig up all the answers.

What is the full name of this person(s)?
When was the photo taken?
Where was it taken?
Why do you think it was taken?
What is (are) the person(s) doing?
Is the clothing in the picture different from today's?
Do(es) the person(s) look happy or sad?
If you are in the picture, do any memories come to mind?

Young Folks and Senior Citizens*

When historians interview senior citizens they ask questions about everyday things such as food, holidays, and raising children. The answers tell historians how people lived in the past.

You can use the cards on the next page to obtain two kinds of information.

1. *Understanding Your Own History—Young Folks.* Answer the questions personally. Have a friend do likewise, then compare answers. How were both of your families alike or different?

2. *Understanding the Good Old Days—Senior Citizens.* Interview some old-timers in your community. A senior citizens' club is a good lead. Grandparents that live near you are also a convenient source. Find some people with interesting back-grounds: people who have lived in other lands; retired doctors, teachers, or factory workers; retired ministers, priests, or rabbis.

*The activities listed under Young Folks and Senior Citizens and Memories were developed and refined as a result of our observations of Jamie Litner, Molly McClaskey, and Douglas Pease doing the activities. We thank them for their help.

Grandma's House
Visiting Grandma (or another relative):

Did you go to Grandma's on a certain day or at a certain time?

How did you get there?

Were children expected to stay with the adults or to play?

Did Grandma cook any special foods?

What games did you play? Were they different from your usual amusements?

Were other relatives usually present?

In what ways were you spoiled by your grandmother or grandfather?

What did you do before you went visiting? Did you dress up?

Do you remember certain objects from your grandmother's house?

The Good Things
Some special things about your childhood:

Who were your best friends?

Did you have friends from faraway places? From the next town or another country?

What did you and your friends do for fun?

Did you play any special games or have any interesting toys?

What do you remember about a relative who was very nice to you?

Who was your favorite teacher in school?

What did you like most about your house?

What did you like most about your city or town?

Special Days
Did you have a special day in your house?

Was this special day Saturday or Sunday or some other day?

Was it a time for the family to get together?

Did religion play a part on Saturday or Sunday?

Were the children expected to entertain themselves more than usual?

Who got up first?

Was it a day for house or yard work?

What did the neighbors do on Saturday or Sunday?

Did you eat a special meal on your special day?

Holidays
How did your family spend holidays?

Was everyone usually home on the holiday?

Did you have the same holiday dinner each year?

Were presents or other surprises a big part of the holiday for you?

Did religion play a part in your celebrations?

Did special friends visit on the holiday?

Punishment
What happened to you when you misbehaved?

How were you punished?

How long did the punishment last?

Why were you punished?

Who was punished the most in your family?

Were the punishments the same for you, your brothers, and your sisters?

Did the punishment fit the misbehavior?

Meals
Your family's eating habits:

Did people always sit in the same place? How was this decided?

What did discussions center around—school, bickering, sharing, work, or friends?

Who served, cleared the table, and did the dishes? How was this decided?

What kind of meals did you have—meat, casseroles, vegetarian, junk food, or international dishes?

Where did you eat your meals?

Was a radio or TV on during meals?

Memories - Events

History books are filled with the events of the past, some interesting, some boring. Historians try to explain the whys of the past by comparing the whats of the past—the memories that different people have about events. A good historian is just like a lawyer who pieces together the actions of the different people present at an accident or crime to explain the event. No one can rediscover *exactly* how things were, but the more we explain about our past, the more we learn about our present and future.

For history that has no living witnesses, historians compare stone tablets, newspapers, books, or any enduring record of the past. They refine, reconcile, and redefine different opinions to come up with an explanation of the way things were.

For recent history, historians gather and study the memories of living people. A historian of World War I or the Depression can contact people who survived these events. Memories are as important as recorded information to the historian.

Here is an activity you can do to try out your skills as a historian. Use our challenge question to get started: *What was your childhood like?*

Gathering the Information

Find ten people of about your age. Give each person five index cards and the following directions:

1. Try to remember five interesting things that happened to you as you were growing up—happy, sad, or exciting events that you won't mind sharing with others.

2. For each event, write a sentence and make a drawing on the front of an index card.

3. Write down your age at the time of the event.

Here are some samples.

Fell off the school bus and broke my knee.

Age 9

Broke my Brothers tooth when I hit him in the mouth

Age 8

Sharing the Information

At the bottom of a bulletin board or chalkboard tape the following signs:

Family Trip	Accident	A Pet
Argument with Brother or Sister	Neighborhood Fun	A Big Suprise
Something Athletic	Something Musical	A Big Disappointment
A holiday	Other	Getting away with Something

Now ask the ten people to tape their event cards above the appropriate signs.

When everyone has finished, study the event cards above the Other sign and classify them in new groups.

Ah, To Be Young Again!

1. Based on the event cards, how would a historian describe childhood for your age group?

2. Discuss the event cards with your friends and think about the events that you had in common.

3. What were the happiest, scariest, and most interesting events put up on the board?

Things

Thing-a-ma-bobs

What kinds of things were people willing to spend their money on in the past? Some places to discover what people bought back in the good old days are an antique shop, where you can talk with the owner about some of the interesting items for sale there, and a library that has a good supply of old magazines filled with advertisements. Old mail order catalogs are clues to the consumerism of the past. Older friends and relatives might still have original mail order catalogs. Some publishers are now reprinting old catalogs, so you may even find

CANDY.

Send for our Special Grocery List, in which we list a full line of candy of every description.

No. 7R1550 Chicago Mixed Candy.
Price per 30-pound pail........................$2.25
Price, per 5-pound box........................ .40

No. 7R1551 Columbia Mixed Candy.
Price, per 30-pound pail........................ 2.95
Price, per 5-pound box........................ .55
Price, per 2-pound box........................ .28

No. 7R1552 Kindergarten Mixed Candy.
Price, per 30-pound pail........................ 2.85
Price, per 5-pound box........................ .53
Price, per 2-pound box........................ .25

No. 7R1553 Gum Drops.
Price, per 30-pound pail........................ 1.75
Price, per 5-pound box........................ .32

No. 7R1554 Licorice Gum Drops.
Price, per 30-pound pail........................ 3.00
Price, per 5-pound box........................ .55

No. 7R1555 French Mixed Candy.
Price, per 30-pound pail........................ 4.60
Price, per 5-pound box........................ .85
Price, per 2-pound box........................ .38
Price, per 1-pound box........................ .20

No. 7R1611 Wintergreen Lozenges, pink and white. Price, per 5-pound box........................59c

No. 7R1612 Conversation Lozenges, assorted. Price, per 5-pound box........................64c

No. 7R1620 Rock Candy, white, best quality. Price, per 5-pound box........................59c

No. 7R1622 Rock Candy, assorted colors. Price, per 5-pound box........................59c

No. 7R1625 Japanese Cocoanut. Price, per box containing 100 strips........................54c

No. 7R1635 Cream Dips, assorted flavors. Price, per 5-pound box........................69c

No. 7R1636 Assorted Bonbons. Price, per 5-pound box........................$1.10

No. 7R1661 Maple Creams. Price, per 5-pound box........................59c

No. 7R1665 Strawberry Creams. Price, per 5-pound box........................59c

No. 7R1670 Flippi Cream Almonds. This is a popular candy, a little larger than a pecan nut, almond center with a heavy coat of pure sugar flavored with vanilla. Price, per 5-pound box...75c

No. 7R1675 Spanish Peanut Stick. Price, per box of 100 bars........................64c

No. 7R1676 Jelly Squares, crystallized. Price, per 5-pound box........................59c

No. 7R1677 Jelly Fruit Beans. Price, per 5-pound box........................50c

Shelled Nuts.

No. 7R1678 Almonds, Jordan, shelled.
Price, 5-pound box, per pound........................47c
Price, less quantities, per pound........................49c

No. 7R1679 Almonds, Taragona, shelled.
Price, 5-pound box........................35c
Price, less quantities, per pound........................37c

No. 7R1680 Peanuts, Spanish, shelled, green.
Price, 100-pound box, per pound........................7½c
Price, less quantities, per pound........................8½c

No. 7R1681 Peanuts, shelled and salted, guaranteed fresh roasted.
Price, 50-pound box, per pound........................9¼c
Price, per 5-pound box,........................50c
Price, per 2-pound box........................22c

Chewing Gum.

We do not sell less than full box.

No. 7R1699 Adams' Black Jack Gum, 5 sticks in package, 20 packages in box. Price, per box......55c

No. 7R1700 Adams' New York Rubber Gum, 400 pieces in a box. Price, per box........................59c

No. 7R1701 Adams' Pepsin Tutti Frutti Gum, 5 squares to the bar, 2 bars to the package, 20 packages to the box. Price, per box........................59c

No. 7R1703 Beeman's Pepsin Gum, 5 pieces to package, 20 packages to box. Price, per box......62c

No. 7R1704 Yankee Spruce Gum, 5 pieces to package, 20 packages to box. Price, per box..... 60c

No. 7R1706 White's Yucatan Gum, 5 pieces to package, 20 packages to box. Price, per box......55c

No. 7R1707 Ripe Fruit Gum, 20 5-cent packages in box. Price, per box........................55c

No. 7R1708 Primley's California Fruit, 20 5-cent packages in box. Price, per box........................59c

No. 7R1709 Kiss Me Gum, 20 5-cent packages in box. Price, per box........................55

If by mail, postage extra, per box, 15 cents.

BOYS' OR YOUTHS' CAPS.

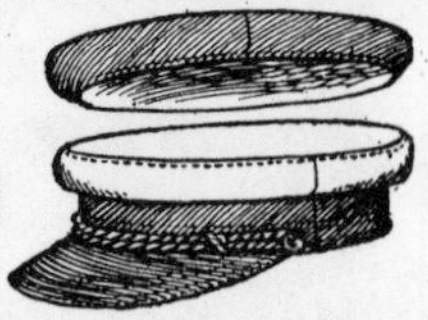

No. 33R2550 Boys' or Youths' Double Cover Fine Yacht Caps. The newest and most practical yacht cap made. The cap proper is made with a fine white duck top. The separate cover is made of blue serge and slips over the white top, making a regular style blue cap. When the separate cover is attached, the point of contact is invisible, having exactly the appearance of a regular blue golf cap. Made in a strictly first class manner throughout with fine leather sweatband. The band, visor and blue detachable cover are made of fine blue wool serge. Navy blue only; an ideal cap for your boy. Sizes, 6⅝ to 7⅛ only.
Price, per dozen, $5.04; each........................42c
If by mail, postage extra, each, 9 cents.

Boys' Navy Blue University Caps.

No. 33R2554 Boys' Finest Navy Blue Broadcloth University Caps. Similar to the golf style, but fuller in the crown, and does not hook down in front; lined with satin. Sizes, 6¼ to 7 only. Warranted first class in every way. Price, each........................45c
If by mail, postage extra, 10 cents.

Boys' Wool Golf Style Hat, 43 Cents.

No. 33R2378 Boys' Golf Style Wool Hat, trimmed with narrow band and leather sweatband; raw edge. A good hat at a very low price. Colors, black or light gray. Sizes, 6¾ to 7 only.
Price, each........................43c
If by mail, postage extra, 16 cents.

Boys' Telescope Hats.

No. 33R2382 Boys' Wool Hat, Telescope Style. Very popular hat, becoming to most boys. Wide silk band, leather sweat band and raw edge. Colors, black, brown or blue. Sizes, 6¼ to 7 only. Price, each........................45c
If by mail, postage extra, 13 cents.

The Roosevelt.

No. 33R2228 Men's Fur Hat, flat set brim, in a good quality fur stock, leather sweatband; narrow silk ribbon band. Crown, 6 inches; brim, 3½ inches, flat set. A fuller shape than the Regulation Cavalry Hats. An excellent hat at our low price. Colors, black and belly nutria. Sizes, 6¾ to 7½. What size do you wear? Price, each..$1.00
If by mail, postage extra, 27 cents.

The Stanley.

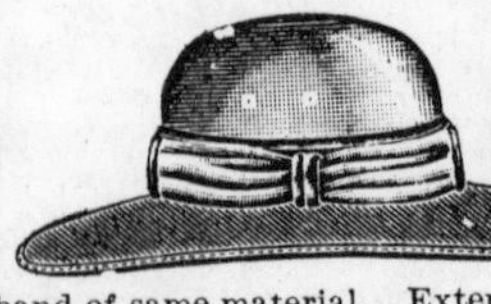

No. 33R3010 This is another of those sensible solid comfort hot weather hats; made with light weight straw crown, covered with colored silesia, trimmed with sash band of same material. Extended sweatband, giving perfect ventilation. Sizes, 6¾ to 7⅜.
Price, per dozen, $4.56; each........................38c
If by mail, postage extra, 22 cents.

If you forget to give size of hat or cap wanted, we cannot fill your order.

For Girls 5 to 10 Years Old.

$1.18

No. 39R154 A very elegantly designed misses' white leghorn hat with fancy straw edge. This is an imported Italian leghorn flat, with fancy new designed crown, trimmed in the front, and slightly to the left are large, elaborate puffs of canary colored silk finished mull and wired loops of silk, satin faced ribbon, wired so as to hold them in place, and the ribbon is caught under the crown and to the bandeau. Tastily arranged in the folds of mull are sprays of full blown light blue lilies of the valley with foliage. A very pretty and effective hat for misses from five to ten years of age. Can be ordered trimmed in light blue, pink, cardinal or white.
Price, each........................$1.18

Genuine Parisian Style.

$5.75

No. 39R155 Elegant Parisian Gainsborough effect dress hat with semi-tam crown. A very elegant hat for stylish dressers. The entire wire frame is covered with white silk mull and overlaid with a black spangled net. The black and white combination of trimming is very stylish and much desired this season. **The semi-tam crown is covered with an exceptionally pretty imported spangled crown. Over the brim and beneath the crown is a fold of black silk velvet, same extending to the back in a large bow and falling over the brim where it is caught on the bandeau. A large black Amazon real ostrich plume of very fine quality and six black satin roses complete the trimming of this richly millinered hat. Well worth $10.00. Can be ordered trimmed as described only.** Price, each........................$5.75

some in a bookstore.

Track down some clues to the year 1902. Look over the sample items from this 1902 Sears, Roebuck & Co. catalog and think about the questions that follow.

Treats

1. Are any of these brands still sold?

2. Which of these treats would have been your favorite?

Hats

1. Do you own a hat? If you do, is it like any of these?

2. Why do you think one of these hats is called the Roosevelt?

3. What is the origin of the name of the Stanley hat? (Hint: Find out what Sir Henry Morton Stanley was famous for. Does the hat look like something he might have worn?)

Wigs

1. Do people still wear wigs?

2. Are any of the "hair" styles still popular?

3. What were the toupees and wigs made of?

4. Why do you think that red, blonde, and gray hair wigs cost extra?

A BEAUTIFUL STYLE FOR
MIDDLE AGED AND ELDERLY LADIES,
A QUALITY REGULAR MILLINERS GET $4.00 TO $5.00 FOR . . . . .
Our $1.95 Bonnet.

No. 39R165 A richly designed hand made bonnet made on a silk wire frame and covered with an imported hair straw lace braid. The trimming in front consists of a profusion of artistically made rosettes of a fine quality of silk mousseline de soie. Directly in the center of the rosette is a cluster of pretty violets with foliage and a large spray of imported aigrettes with fancy spangles. Long ties of all silk satin faced ribbon completes the trimming of this very tasty and becoming bonnet suitable for middle aged and elderly ladies. Black only. Price, each $1.95

How to Measure a Wig.
State style of wig, kind of parting, whether for right or left side; price and description as per list; to insure a good fit mention number of inches. Send sample of hair. Inches.
No. 1 Circumference of head....
No. 2 Forehead to nape of neck. ..
No. 3 Ear to ear, across forehead ..
No. 4 Ear to ear, over top... ......
No. 5 Temple to temple, round back............

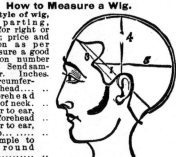

Men's Toupees

To measure for a Toupee or top piece, cut a piece of paper the exact size and shape of the bald spot, mark the crown and parting, enclose a lock of hair, and state if hair is to be straight or curly.
No. 18R4418 Men's Toupee, weft foundation. Price, each..(If by mail, postage extra, 8c)..$5.50
No. 18R4422 Men's Toupee, ventilated foundation. Price, each.............................$10.00

Gentlemen's Wigs.

Gentlemen's Wigs are made of the finest selected hair. We guarantee our work the highest grade, and they cannot be distinguished from the natural growth. If by mail, postage extra, each, 8 cents.
No. 18R4426 Men's Full Wigs. Weft with crown, cotton foundation. Price, each................$8.00
No. 18R4430 Men's Full Wigs. Gauze or silk parting. Price, each........................$12.00
No. 18R4434 Men's Wigs. Ventilated with hair net parting. Price, each. $21.00
Red, Blonde and Gray Hair cost extra; allow one-half more than above prices.

WAVES, BANGS AND WIGS.
All Wigs, Toupees, Waves, etc., being made to order, we ask three to four days' time in filling your order, and we require cash in full with order as on all other merchandise, guaranteeing satisfaction or refund of money.
BE SURE AND SEND A GOOD SIZED SAMPLE OF HAIR.
No. 18R4378 Melba Bang. Made of the best quality naturally curly hair, with vegetable lace parting, most suitable for youthful faces and a very popular style of hair dressing. Each $1.50
Gray and blonde hair, each...................... 2.50
If by mail, postage extra, each, 5 cents.

Parisian Bang.
No. 18R4382 Parisian Bang. Ladies who do not require large, heavy front, will find this a little gem; light and fluffy, ventilated foundation. Price, each.....$1.35
Gray and blonde hair, each $2.00
If by mail, postage extra, each, 5 cents.

Alice Wave.

No. 18R4386 Alice Wave, invisible hair lace; foundation natural, curly hair; 3-inch part, 12 inches from side to side. Price, each...................$3.25
Gray and blonde hair, each............ 4.50
If by mail, postage extra, each, 6 cents.

The Pompadour.
No. 18R4390 The Pompadour. This style, unlike the old style pompadour, is very light in weight. The soft wavy hair is combed over one's own hair in which small rolls of crape hair are placed to produce a puffy effect on sides and top.
Price, each.....................$3.50
Gray and blonde hair, each...................... 5.00
If by mail, postage extra, each, 6 cents.

The Patent Pompadour.
No. 18R4394 The Patent Pompadour for simplicity, elegance and style is far superior to anything ever shown. It slips right on, is as dainty as a feminine heart could desire; it produces the fluffy fullness now so much in vogue and possesses none of the disagreeable qualities of the ordinary roll or pad. It is made on twisted wire, of the best long, curly hair and weighs only half an ounce. Send sample of hair. Price, each.............. $1.50
If by mail, postage extra, each, 6 cents.

The Eugenia Wave.
No. 18R4398 The Eugenia Wave. This is a new and very becoming wave for middle aged and elderly ladies, made of the best quality natural curly French hair; easily dressed and cared for; 3½-inch parting.
Price, each...$4.00
Gray and blonde hair, each.....$6.00
If by mail, postage extra, each, 8 cents.

Ladies' Wigs—Short Hair
Send measurement of head.

These wigs are all made of fine selected hair on ventilated open mesh foundation. Absolutely perfect in fit, having that graceful and natural appearance.
No. 18R4402 Ladies' Curly Dress Wig, made of natural short hair, with or without part, mounted on fine open mesh cotton foundation.
Each... $10.00
Gray or blonde hair, each, $15.00

Short Curly Wig.
If by mail, postage extra, each, 14 cents.
No. 18R4406 Ladies' Wig. Same as above but mounted on silk foundation. Price, each....$12.00
Gray or blonde hair, each...................... 18.00
If by mail, postage extra, each, 8 cents.

Ladies' Wigs—Long Hair.
Can be arranged in many different ways.
No. 18R4410 Made of the best selected hair on silk foundation, 18-inch hair.
Price, each $15.00
If by mail, postage extra, each, 10 cents.
No. 18R4414 Made same as above on silk foundation, 24-inch hair.
Price, each.........$18.00
If by mail, postage extra, each, 10 cents.
The above prices are for ordinary shades hair. Red, Blonde and Gray Hair cost 50 per cent more, which please add when you send order. Be sure and send sample of hair. Send measurement of head.

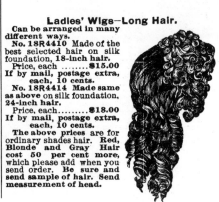

Clothing
1. Did people dress in a fancier way in 1902 than they do today?
2. What kinds of materials were used in the clothing? Are the fabrics natural or made by people?
3. Do you think that these clothes were comfortable?

Cures
1. What problems were people trying to remedy?
2. Can you find a cure for a dope addict here?
3. Do you think that any of these cures worked?

Beautiful Double Shoulder Cape, $1.69.

No. 38R1880
A beautiful Double Cape, made of all wool Shetland yarn, lower and upper cape trimmed with Shetland yarn in the form of small squares, upper cape trimmed with silk floss, trimmed around neck, down front and bottom with small pompons made of Shetland floss (front and lower part of both capes trimmed this way), strings and tassels at neck. Length, upper cape, 10 inches; lower cape, 15 inches; sweep, 80 inches. Color, cream with blue or pink trimmings.
Price. each...................$1.69

AN ALL WOOL NAVY BLUE CHEVIOT makes a very handsome vestee suit. We think that the suit shown by the opposite illustration is one of the nicest and prettiest vestee suits ever shown by any house. Especially is it a handsome suit when you consider the price. Made with a new style round cut coat; vest is made double breasted style with a red flannel dickey, silk monogram worked in center of dickey. The pants are made double seat and double at knees. The suit is extra well trimmed and finished throughout.
No. 40R78 Price for boys' three-piece vestee suit for boys aged 3 to 8 years........$2.00

All Wool Light Tan and Brown Mixed Cheviot Suit, $2.50.

THIS IS ONE OF THE HANDSOMEST LIGHT COLORED SUITS IN OUR LINE. The suit is made of an all wool cheviot in a tan and light brown coloring. It has an almost invisible over plaid effect in dark green and red. The suit is made the new style imitation double breasted coat. The lapels are faced in satin. The vest is made single breasted style with a tan flannel dickey to match material in suit. The pants are made double seat and double at knees. Garments are well sewed.
No. 40R80 Price for boys' three-piece vestee suit, for boys aged 3 to 8 years............$2.50

No. 31R336
$3.50

No. 31R386 VERY NOBBY WASH SUIT. Consisting of waist and skirt, made of very fine lawn in striped patterns, the waist is trimmed with wide lace in front, on sleeves and on the high standing collar; lace trimming in back forms a pointed yoke; the skirt is made with a graduated flounce trimmed with lace; this flounce is over the skirt, leaving a dust ruffle under the flounce; a very neat and most desirable suit for the summer. Colors, black and white, and pink and white, striped pattern.
Price. .... (If by mail, postage extra, 26 cents)............. $3.50

No. 38R2105 A VERY STYLISH CHILD'S DRESS, made of good quality of madras cloth, yoke made of white pique trimmed with six pearl buttons, straps on each side at waist, trimmed with pearl buttons, has embroidery insertion in front and back over shoulders, followed with a ruffle of wide embroidery. Extra good value. Colors, blue or pink stripes.
Price.............. (If by mail, postage extra, 10 cents)............$1.25

No. 38R2106 THE VERY NEWEST PRINCESS STYLE CHILD'S DRESS, made of madras, has a very pretty round yoke made with three rows of embroidery insertion and tucks, embroidery and ribbon insertion both front and back, followed with a ruffle of same material as in dress, which is edged with embroidery, large ribbon bow, embroidery and ribbon insertion at flounce, collar and cuffs edged with embroidery, wide hem at bottom. Colors, pink and white or blue and white. Price............$1.48
If by mail, postage extra, 12 cents.

Stein & Co.'s All Wool Worsted Suit, $7.00.

A dark brown and navy blue mixture formed in a medium sized checked pattern. A handsome, fine, extra quality, hard finished worsted goods, cloth that will wear, hold color and give perfect satisfaction. The coat is made in round cut sack style, vest is cut single breasted with collar. Pants have two side, two hip and one watch pocket.
No. 40R34 Price for boys' long pants suit, style 1. ...... $7.00

Tallcott & Co.'s Gray Mixed Covert Suit, $7.50.

This is a handsome, light colored gray covert cassimere with a red overplaid, especially for spring and summer wear. If you want a handsome, up to date, very fine suit, we especially recommend this number, as we are sure you will be more than pleased with it. The suit is made with a round cut sack coat well trimmed and lined throughout, vest is double breasted, no collar; pants have two hip, two side and one watch pocket.
No. 40R36 Price for boys' long pants suit, style 1.....$7.50

Our Finest All Worsted Fancy Suit, $8.00.

At $8.00 we offer you a suit of a finer quality than is ordinarily kept in the best retail stores. We recommend our $8.00 suit because you can appreciate the extra fine quality of the goods, the fine linings, the well made garments that we can furnish you at this price, value that will guarantee our securing your future patronage. This suit is made of a very fine all worsted cloth in a dark green and navy blue broken checked pattern. The coat is made in round sack style. The vest is made single breasted. The pants have two side, two hip and one watch pocket. If you order this or any other number in our long pants suits and you are not satisfied that you have gotten the best value you ever had for the money you are at liberty to return it to us and we will cheerfully refund your money.
No. 40R38 Price for boys long pants suits, style 1 only. .$8.00

STYLE 1

Sure Cure for the Tobacco Habit.

Retail price .... 50c and $1.00
Our price, 50c size, each $0.40
Our price, 50c size, per dozen 3.60
Our price, $1.00 size, each .... .75
Our price, $1.00 size, per dozen 6.60

WE CURE YOU This is nature's own remedy, entirely harmless. It cures because it builds up and fortifies, rejuvenates the weak and unstrung nerves caused by over indulgence in this poisonous weed. It stops the craving for tobacco by supplying instead a healthy nerve tonic and strengthener; it does more, it eradicates the poisonous nicotine from the system which has accumulated from long continued use of tobacco. Nicotine is a virulent poison and the chief ingredient of tobacco. It is the cause of all the **nervous troubles** and general debility of smokers. Our sure cure will destroy the effects of this nicotine, chase it from the system and make weak men strong again, and impotent men gain weight and vigor, make the old feel young again. It satisfies the **craving for tobacco**, and its use brings great health, increasing the appetite for food, strengthens the stomach, enriches and purifies the blood, giving good general health. It is not a drug; **it can be chewed the same as tobacco**, or taken dissolved in coffee or hot water. It is not only a **sure cure for the tobacco habit**, but also one of the best tonics for sexual weakness ever made. Give it a trial and be convinced

> You can cure yourself and others from the tobacco habit. Order a supply at our special quantity prices. You can sell them easily at a good profit.

No. 8R1 Price, regular size box, per dozen, $3.60; each 40c
No. 8R2 Price, large box, per dozen, $6.60; each 75c
If by mail, postage extra per box, small, 2 cents; large, 4 cents.

Somone, for Sweet, Refreshing Sleep.

Retail price $1.50
Our price, each $0.67
Our price, per dozen 6.00

A RELIABLE REMEDY FOR SLEEPLESSNESS. We ask any of our customers who may be troubled with insomnia, who cannot sleep at night, to give this valuable remedy a trial. No matter from what cause the sleeplessness arises, a sound sleep will be procured by its use, and you will awake in the morning refreshed, strengthened and cheerful; no bad effects from its use. We guarantee it to contain no opium, morphine or poisonous narcotics of any kind whatever. It is a vegetable preparation composed of herbs soothing and healing to the entire system. It can be used in safety by the weakest and most delicate and is a boon to those of nervous dispositions. A single dose will strengthen and invigorate them and cause them to forget their troubles. Ladies troubled with nervous spells should always have a bottle at hand. A dose or two in time will save them many hours of agony and serious discomfort and often prevent total collapse of the nervous system. It has a marvelous effect on those afflicted with nervous prostration, acting like magic in restoring the nerves to their normal condition and causing a strong healthy feeling to prevail throughout the whole body. It quiets the nervous excitement and muscular trembling caused by the excessive use of liquor, and acts as an antidote to the liquor habit. Full directions accompany each bottle how to use it both for sleeplessness and nervous troubles.

> DO NOT FAIL TO INCLUDE THIS REMEDY IN YOUR QUANTITY ORDER. THOUSANDS OF PATIENTS NEED IT AND BUY IT.

No. 8R5 Price, per dozen bottles, $6.00; each 67c
Cannot be sent by mail on account of weight.

Mexican Headache Cure.

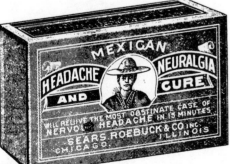

Retail price 25c
Our price, each . $0.17
Our price, per doz. 1.50

A SPLITTING HEADACHE CURED IMMEDIATELY by our positive Headache and Neuralgia Cure. Almost everyone is more or less troubled with a headache at some time or other. Some persons are hardly ever free from them, and suffer martyrdom. We confidently say to our customers that it is not necessary to suffer longer than the time it takes to get a package of our **Mexican Headache Cure.** We positively guarantee relief within fifteen minutes after the first dose has been taken. Rarely is a second dose required except in very obstinate cases. No matter from what cause, whether a nervous headache, or from the stomach, or a severe case of neuralgia, we guarantee complete relief. It is perfectly harmless, no bad results follow its use. Give it a trial when you suffer, and you will be sure to speak of us as your friends.

> Who does not suffer from headaches occasionally? You can sell this cure to everybody you meet. Many customers who are now in charge of a distributing point for our orders are sending twelve dozen orders at one time.

No. 8R8 Price, per box $0.17
Per dozen boxes 1.50
If by mail, postage extra, per box, 2 cents.

German Liquor Habit Cure.

Retail price .... 50c and $1.00
Our price, 50c size, each $0.42
Our price, 50c size, per dozen 3.60
Our price, $1.00 size, each .... .75
Our price, $1.00 size, per dozen 6.60

Every Man Can be Permanently Cured of the Habit or Desire for Intoxicating Drink of Any Kind.

WE GUARANTEE A COMPLETE CURE. Our remedy is perfectly harmless, none of the bad effects produced by many so-called liquor cures so widely advertised. That drunkenness is a disease that can be cured by medicine, just the same as other diseases can, is a fact becoming well known. Thousands of cases have been cured by this medicine; in fact, its wonderful curative properties are now well known throughout the entire world. We bring this cure within the reach of everyone. It is now not necessary to go to an institute for treatment; home treatment is just as successful. The impression has been cultivated by interested parties that cures could not be effected except by hypodermic injections, but nothing is more absurd. Any medicine taken into the stomach will be as effective as if used hypodermically. No medicine has had such a wonderful success in this age of progress as Our Liquor Habit Cure. It creates an appetite for food instead of liquor, it stimulates the whole system to healthy action, it quiets nervous excitement, vertigo, muscular trembling and all the dangerous effects of excessive use of liquor. It improves the appetite and digestion and regulates the bowels. It is, in fact, a perfect cure for the drink habit. We urge everyone who have accustomed themselves to the excessive use of liquor, and who wish to stop the practice, to send for even a small box as a trial. We know our remedy will cure you. We are sure that after using a few doses you will feel the craving for liquor disappearing and a warm healthy glow spreading from the stomach over the whole system; you will have a desire for food instead of whisky. This will be the commencement of the cure, and if you will follow it up faithfully for a few months it will effect a permanent cure. When you have used a small box, we know you will send for more to thoroughly complete the cure.

> YOU CAN SELL LARGE QUANTITIES OF THIS REMEDY. IT WILL ALWAYS DO THE WORK, AND RECOMMENDS ITSELF WHEREVER USED.

No. 8R11 Price, small box containing 24 doses, per dozen, $3.60; each .42c
No. 8R12 Price, large box containing 48 doses, per dozen, $6.60; each .75c
If by mail, postage, extra, per box, small, 2 cents; large, 4 cents.

Cure for the Opium and Morphia Habit.

Retail price $1.50
Our price, each $0.67
Our price, per dozen 6.00

WE HERE OFFER A PERFECTLY SAFE AND RELIABLE CURE

to those addicted to the habit of using opium or morphia in any form or manner whatever. We guarantee this preparation to be absolutely harmless, to contain no poisonous narcotics. Can be taken freely without producing any of the deleterious effects on the system, such as are caused by the use of opium and morphia. Immediately on taking a dose of this remedy a calming and soothing effect is produced. It acts as a tonic to the nerves; its use will completely destroy that terrible craving for morphine in those who are victims to the deadly habit of taking these poisonous drugs, and free them from their bondage, restoring their health and making them feel like living again. A dose can be taken whenever a craving for morphia or opium exists; it will act at first as a perfect substitute, rendering the patient independent of these poisonous drugs, and after continued use for a short period the nerves will become strong and the general health improved, so that the remedy can be taken at longer intervals and soon altogether discontinued; then the cure is complete.

No. 8R15 Price, per dozen bottles, $6.00; each 67c
Cannot be sent by mail on account of weight.

Fat Folks, Take Dr. Rose's Obesity Powders and Watch the Result.

Retail price 75c
Our price, each $0.50
Our price, per dozen .. 4.20

TOO MUCH FAT is a disease and a source of great annoyance to those afflicted. It impairs the strength and produces fatty degeneration of the heart, and sudden death results. All people who have obesity are troubled with sluggish circulation and labored action of the heart. The patient feels lazy and burdensome. There is a sluggish condition of the whole system; they are not exactly sickly, there is a feeling that all is not right. Nervousness, rheumatism, headache, dropsy and kidney diseases are frequent complications of obesity, and, more cause to be alarmed, the heart is always affected. Send at once for a box of Dr. Rose's Obesity Cure. It will reduce corpulence in a safe and agreeable manner, per-

> A boon to fat people who will be glad to obtain this remedy at home when they know you keep it on hand ......

fectly harmless. No bad results follow its use, as is the case with many of the much advertised cures. Explicit directions and valuable information for fat folks enclosed in each box.

No. 8R18 Price, per dozen boxes, $4.20; per box 50c
If by mail, postage extra, per box, 2 cents.

Tombstone Territory
MESSAGES FROM THE PAST*

Have you ever thought of visiting a cemetery to find out about the past? In a way, a cemetery is a place in which people who have died can share messages with us. The study of the gravestones, or tombstones, in a cemetery will inform you about the people who once lived in your city or town. For different time periods, you can learn about

1. *Individual and average life spans*

2. *Number of children in the typical family*

3. *Accidents that caused death*

4. *Diseases that caused death*

5. *Epitaphs, or sentences on gravestones, that indicate how the people wanted to be remembered*

6. *Current religious beliefs . . . and much, much more.*

At the right is a guide to more of the things you can discover in a cemetery. It's a diagram called a web or flow chart. You may wish to add your own ideas to it.

*The activities listed under Tombstone Territory were developed and refined as a result of our conversations with Charles Rathbone, Wayne Tarr, and Frank Watson of the University of Vermont. We thank them for their help.

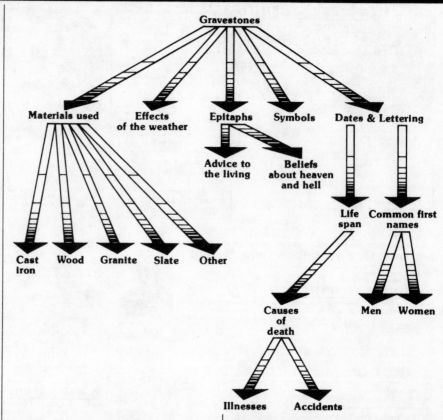

Abstracted and adapted from a comprehensive flow chart on cemetery history developed by Dr. Charles Rathbone, University of Vermont, Burlington, Vt.

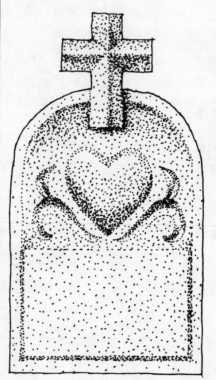

Tombstone Symbols

Symbol	Name	Meaning
	Heart	Love of the soul for God
	Winged death head	Death winning out over life
	Dove	Carrier of the Holy Spirit
	Angel	Heaven
	Living things (trees, flowers, palm leaves)	Life
	Grapes	Represent wine, which symbolizes the blood of Christ in Christian religions

Tombstone Territory Guide Sheet

Add your own questions to this chart and take it with you when you visit a cemetery.

_____

What year is the oldest gravestone?

What year is the newest gravestone?

What is the most interesting epitaph?

What wars in our history are mentioned on the gravestones?

In family plots, who usually died first, the husband or wife?

What were some interesting first names?

_____

Don't Overlook the Symbols

On the flow chart, you probably noticed the "symbols" category. Many people consider the symbols on gravestones to be merely the artistic touches of stone cutters. These long-forgotten stone cutters sometimes left us messages in their symbols, some of which we can "decode." Above is a chart of six symbols that you may find on very old gravestones. In the blank spaces, draw in other interesting ones that you discover. Local clergymen or gravestone carvers may be able to tell you about the meanings of the symbols.

Cemetery Manners

The solemnity of a cemetery should be respected by all who visit it. Loudness and roudiness are out of place there. Be sure to walk on the paths provided and not on the graves themselves. Other people who come to visit the grave sites of friends or relatives will appreciate your acting in a dignified way.

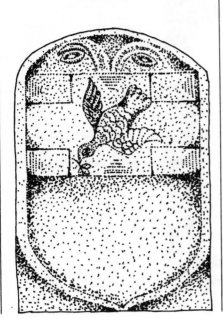
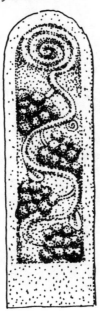

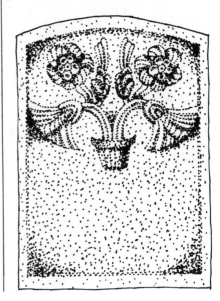

What was the front page like on your birthday?

"All the News That's Fit to Print"

The New York Times

LATE CITY EDITION
Weather: Rain, warm today; clear tonight. Sunny, pleasant tomorrow. Temp. range: today 80-66; Sunday 71-66. Temp.-Hum. Index yesterday 69. Complete U.S. report on P. 50.

VOL. CXVIII. No. 40,721   © 1969 The New York Times Company   NEW YORK, MONDAY, JULY 21, 1969   10 CENTS

MEN WALK ON MOON

ASTRONAUTS LAND ON PLAIN; COLLECT ROCKS, PLANT FLAG

Voice From Moon: 'Eagle Has Landed'

EAGLE (the lunar module): Houston, Tranquility Base here. The Eagle has landed.

HOUSTON: Roger, Tranquility, we copy you on the ground. You've got a bunch of guys about to turn blue. We're breathing again. Thanks a lot.

TRANQUILITY BASE: Thank you.

HOUSTON: You're looking good here.

TRANQUILITY BASE: A very smooth touchdown.

HOUSTON: Eagle, you are stay for T1. [The first step in the lunar operation.] Over.

TRANQUILITY BASE: Roger. Stay for T1.

HOUSTON: Roger and we see you venting the ox.

TRANQUILITY BASE: Roger.

COLUMBIA (the command and service module): How do you read me?

HOUSTON: Columbia, he has landed Tranquility Base. Eagle is at Tranquility. I read you five by. Over.

COLUMBIA: Yes, I heard the whole thing.

HOUSTON: Well, it's a good show.

COLUMBIA: Fantastic.

TRANQUILITY BASE: I'll second that.

APOLLO CONTROL: The next major stay-no stay will be for the T2 event. That is at 21 minutes 26 seconds after initiation of power descent.

COLUMBIA: Up telemetry command reset to re-acquire on high gain.

HOUSTON: Copy. Out.

APOLLO CONTROL: We have an unofficial time for that touchdown of 102 hours, 45 minutes, 42 seconds and we will update that.

HOUSTON: Eagle, you loaded R2 wrong. We want 10254.

TRANQUILITY BASE: Roger. Do you want the horizontal 55 15.2?

HOUSTON: That's affirmative.

APOLLO CONTROL: We're now less than four minutes from our next stay-no stay. It will be for one complete revolution of the command module.

One of the first things that Armstrong and Aldrin will do after getting their next stay-no stay will be to remove their helmets and gloves.

HOUSTON: Eagle, you are stay for T2. Over.

Continued on Page 4, Col. 1

VOYAGE TO THE MOON

By ARCHIBALD MACLEISH

PRESENCE among us,
    wanderer in our skies,

dazzle of silver in our leaves and on our
    waters silver,

O
silver evasion in our farthest thought—
    "the visiting moon" . . . "the glimpses of the moon" . . .

and we have touched you!

        From the first of time,
before the first of time, before the
first men tasted time, we thought of you.
You were a wonder to us, unattainable,
a longing past the reach of longing,
a light beyond our light, our lives—perhaps
a meaning to us . . .

        Now
our hands have touched you in your depth of night.

Three days and three nights we journeyed,
steered by farthest stars, climbed outward,
crossed the invisible tide-rip where the floating dust
falls one way or the other in the void between,
followed that other down, encountered
cold, faced death—unfathomable emptiness . . .

Then, the fourth day evening, we descended,
made fast, set foot at dawn upon your beaches,
sifted between our fingers your cold sand.

We stand here in the dusk, the cold, the silence . . .

and here, as at the first of time, we lift up our heads.
Over us, more beautiful than the moon,
a moon, a wonder to us, unattainable,
a longing past the reach of longing,
a light beyond our light, our lives—perhaps
a meaning to us . . .

        O, a meaning!

over us on these silent beaches the bright
    earth,

    presence among us

Neil A. Armstrong moves away from the leg of the landing craft after taking the first step on the surface of the moon

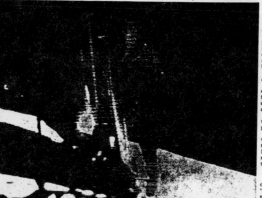

Col. Edwin E. Aldrin Jr. climbing down the ladder. The television camera was attached to a side of the lunar module.

The New York Times from C.B.S. News

Mr. Armstrong, right, and Colonel Aldrin raise the U.S. flag. A metal rod at right angles to the mast keeps flag unfurled.

Associated Press

A Powdery Surface Is Closely Explored

By JOHN NOBLE WILFORD
Special to The New York Times

HOUSTON, Monday, July 21—Men have landed and walked on the moon.

Two Americans, astronauts of Apollo 11, steered their fragile four-legged lunar module safely and smoothly to the historic landing yesterday at 4:17:40 P.M., Eastern daylight time.

Neil A. Armstrong, the 38-year-old civilian commander, radioed to earth and the mission control room here:

"Houston, Tranquility Base here. The Eagle has landed."

The first men to reach the moon—Mr. Armstrong and his co-pilot, Col. Edwin E. Aldrin Jr. of the Air Force—brought their ship to rest on a level, rock-strewn plain near the southwestern shore of the arid Sea of Tranquility.

About six and a half hours later, Mr. Armstrong opened the landing craft's hatch, stepped slowly down the ladder and declared as he planted the first human footprint on the lunar crust:

"That's one small step for man, one giant leap for mankind."

His first step on the moon came at 10:56:20 P.M., as a television camera outside the craft transmitted his every move to an awed and excited audience of hundreds of millions of people on earth.

Tentative Steps Test Soil

Mr. Armstrong's initial steps were tentative tests of the lunar soil's firmness and of his ability to move about easily in his bulky white spacesuit and backpacks and under the influence of lunar gravity, which is one-sixth that of the earth.

"The surface is fine and powdery," the astronaut reported. "I can pick it up loosely with my toe. It does adhere in fine layers like powdered charcoal to the sole and sides of my boots. I only go in a small fraction of an inch, maybe an eighth of an inch. But I can see the footprints of my boots in the treads in the fine sandy particles."

After 19 minutes of Mr. Armstrong's testing, Colonel Aldrin joined him outside the craft.

The two men got busy setting up another television camera out from the lunar module, planting an American flag into the ground, scooping up soil and rock samples, deploying scientific experiments and hopping and loping about in a demonstration of their lunar agility.

They found walking and working on the moon less taxing than had been forecast. Mr. Armstrong once reported he was "very comfortable."

And people back on earth found the black-and-white television pictures of the bug-shaped lunar module and the men tramping about it so sharp and clear as to seem unreal, more like a toy and toy-like figures than human beings on the most daring and far-reaching expedition thus far undertaken.

Nixon Telephones Congratulations

During one break in the astronauts' work, President Nixon congratulated them from the White House in what he said, "certainly has to be the most historic telephone call ever made."

"Because of what you have done," the President told the astronauts, "the heavens have become a part of man's world. And as you talk to us from the Sea of Tranquility it requires us to redouble our efforts to bring peace and tranquility to earth.

"For one priceless moment in the whole history of man all the people on this earth are truly one—one in their pride in what you have done and one in our prayers that you will return safely to earth."

Mr. Armstrong replied:

"Thank you Mr. President. It's a great honor and privilege for us to be here representing not only the United States but men of peace of all nations, men with interests and a curiosity and men with a vision for the future."

Mr. Armstrong and Colonel Aldrin returned to their landing craft and closed the hatch at 1:12 A.M., 2 hours 21 minutes after opening the hatch on the moon. While the third member of the crew, Lieut. Col. Michael Collins of the Air Force, kept his orbital vigil overhead in the command ship, the two moon explorers settled down to sleep.

Outside their vehicle the astronauts had found a bleak

Continued on Pages 2, Col. 1

Today's 4-Part Issue of The Times

This morning's issue of The New York Times is divided into four parts. The first part is devoted to news of Apollo 11 and includes Editorials and letters to the Editor (Page 16). Poems on the landing on the moon appear on Page 17.

General news begins on the first page of the second part. The News Summary and Index is on the first page of the third part, which includes sports news, obituaries (Page 51) and transportation news and weather reports (Pages 50 and 52).

Financial and business news begins on the first page of the fourth part.

Following is the News Index for today's issue:

	Page		Page
Bills at Washington	36	Food	42
Books	33	Music	42
Bridge	32	Music	38-41
Business	53-56	Obituaries	51
Chess	40	Society	37
Crossword	32	Sports	43-47
Editorials	16	Theaters	38-41
Fashions	37	Transportation	50, 52
Financial	53-56	TV and Radio	47
		Weather	50

News Summary and Index, Page 15

Other Trails to Follow

BIRTHDAY HISTORY/ HERSTORY

Have you ever wondered what the state of the world was on the day that you were born? No? Well, think about it. What kind of world did you enter?

Get out your gumshoes and do a little historical detective work. For permission to read through a copy of a newspaper printed on your birth date, go to your town library or your local newspaper's main office, if the library doesn't keep old copies of newspapers.

"Classified" Information

1. What was the weather like?

2. What was the front page headline?

3. How much did the paper cost?

4. What was the editorial about?

5. What were the letters to the editor about?

6. What were the latest fashions for men and women? (Check the clothing stores advertisements.)

7. What was on special at the food markets and how much did they cost?

8. What crimes were reported?

9. What jobs and salaries were available? (Check the classified section.)

10. What kinds of homes were for sale and at what prices? (Again, check the classified section.)

11. What sporting events were in the news?

12. What movies were playing?

13. In general, how was the world faring on the day that you were born? Do you think things are better now or worse?

Relatives

Ask your parents, aunts, uncles, and grandparents where all your relatives live. Make as long and complete a list of relatives and cities as possible. If some relatives live in other countries, add them to the list. Locate each city on a world map. For small cities, just locate the general area.

It's All Relative

1. Do your relatives live close to each other, or are they scattered?

2. Do your relatives prefer large cities or small towns?

3. Do you have any relatives that live near large bodies of water? Mountains?

4. Which of your relatives live(s) farthest away from you? Nearest?

5. Which of your relatives live(s) in a place that you would like to visit? That you would like to stay away from?

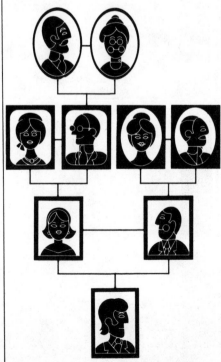

History/Herstory Books

Beable, William Henry. *Epitaphs: Graveyard Humor and Eulogy.* Detroit: Singing Tree Press, 1971.

Boatner, Mark Mayo. *Landmarks of the American Revolution: A Guide to Locating and Knowing What Happened at the Sites of Independence.* Harrisburg, Pa.: Stackpole Books, 1973.

d'Iberville-Moreau, Luc. *Lost Montreal.* Toronto: Oxford University Press, 1975.

Hale, Richard Walden. *Guide to Photocopied Historical Materials in the United States and Canada.* Ithaca, N.Y.: Cornell University Press, 1961.

Hanks, Carole. *Early Ontario Gravestones.* Toronto: McGraw-Hill Ryerson, 1974.

Hilowitz, Beverly, ed. *Great Historical Places of Europe.* New York: American Heritage Publishing, 1974. Distributed by McGraw-Hill.

Jacobs, G. Walker. *Stranger, Stop and Cast an Eye: A Guide to Gravestones and Gravestone Rubbings.* Brattleboro, Vt.: Stephen Greene Press, 1973.

Ludwig, Allan I. *Graven Images: New England Stonecarving and Its Symbols.* Middletown, Conn.: Wesleyan University Press, 1966.

Mann, Thomas Clifford. *Over Their Dead Bodies: Yankee Epitaphs and History.* Brattleboro, Vt.: Stephen Greene Press, 1962.

_____. *Sudden and Awful: American Epitaphs and the Finger of God.* Brattleboro, Vt.: Stephen Greene Press, 1968.

Rifkind, Carole, and Levine, Carol. *Mansions, Mills, and Main Streets.* New York: Schocken Books, 1975.

Robinson, William F. *Abandoned New England: Its Hidden Ruins and Where to Find Them.* New York: New York Graphic Society, 1976.

Schevill, Ferdinand. *Six Historians.* Chicago: University of Chicago Press, 1956.

Spiegl, Fritz, comp. *A Small Book of Grave Humor: Comic and Curious Memorial Inscriptions.* New York: Arco Publishing, 1973.

Stanforth, Deidre. *Restored America.* New York: Praeger Publishing, 1975.

Sternsher, Bernard. *Consensus, Conflict, and American Historians.* Bloomington: Indiana University Press, 1975.

Swann, Don. *Colonial and Historic Houses of Maryland: One Hundred Etchings.* Baltimore: Johns Hopkins University Press, 1975.

The Heritage of New York: Historic Landmark Plaques of the New York Community Trust. New York: Fordam University Press, 1970. This includes "Walking Guide to the Heritage of New York," which is inserted in the book.

Unrau, Harlan D. *Here Was the Revolution: Historic Sites of the War for American Independence.* Washington, D.C.: Department of the Interior, 1976. For sale by the Superintendent of Documents, Government Printing Office.

Wasserman, Emily. *Gravestone Designs: Rubbing and Photographs From Early New York and New Jersey.* New York: Dover Publications, 1972.

Whitehill, Walter Muir. *Boston: Distinguished Buildings and Sites.* Boston: David R. Godine, 1971.

8

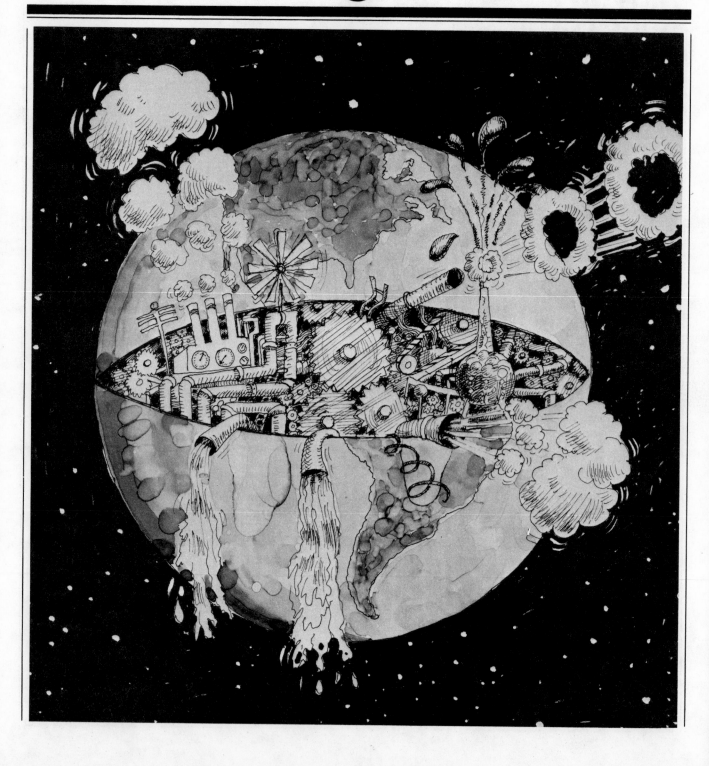

The Dynamic Earth

Swirling cloud movements catch the eye of an astronaut whose spacecraft is entering the atmosphere. An earthquake sends out shock waves that terrify people and crumble buildings. A well of water roars down a river valley and floods a sleepy town. An airline pilot spots a giant thundercloud ahead and quickly swerves the jet out of its way. The quiet earth, our home, is not as peaceful as it seems.

An Interview With Eratosthenes,
THE FIRST PERSON TO MEASURE THE EARTH

Eratosthenes was a Greek geographer who lived from about 276 to 194 B.C. His estimate of the earth's circumference (the distance around the earth) was surprisingly accurate. With the aid of our imaginary time machine, let's travel back to the time of Eratosthenes to interview this man and find out how he arrived at his estimate.

Earthpeople Book: Eratosthenes, tell us, how did you figure out a way to measure the earth?

Eratosthenes: Actually, it was very easy. In the great library at Alexandria I read that a deep vertical well near Syene, in southern Egypt, is entirely lit up by the sun once a year at noon.

Earthpeople Book: How did this information help you?

Eratosthenes: Well, I figured that at noon the sun must be directly overhead in Syene, with its rays shining straight into the well. In Alexandria, which is due north of Syene, I know that the sun is *not* directly overhead at noon on the same day.

Earthpeop!e Book: How do you know that?

Eratosthenes: Because a vertical object like a stick in the ground casts a shadow!

Earthpeople Book: Oh.

Eratosthenes: Knowing this, I could now measure the earth.

Earthpeople Book: How did you do it?

Eratosthenes: I made two assumptions: First, the earth is round, and second, the sun's rays are parallel. I then set up a stick in Alexandria and measured the angle of the sun's shadow when the well at Syene was completely sunlit.

Earthpeople Book: How did this angle help you determine the circumference of the earth?

Eratosthenes: Well, I knew from geometry that this angle represented the angle of the earth's center between Syene and Alexandria. I

The Disaster Game

Have you ever felt the shock waves of an earthquake? Seen a volcano erupt? Heard or seen a tornado? Had your home flooded? Been in the path of an avalanche or rock slide?

The dynamic earth has been producing earthquakes, building up volcanic mountains, flooding the land with water, and creating many changes in our lives for millions of years. Because the earth's human population has reached such high levels, the chances are greater that more and more of *us will be affected by these natural changes. Some of them are good but many cause harm, threatening both life and property. Although we cannot prevent many of these events, precautions and warning systems can save lives.*

The Disaster Game will help you learn about natural disasters and how to respond to them. The directions, the gameboard, and the cards for the game are located in the appendix.

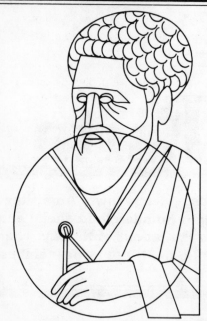

also knew that the arc of this angle was equal to one fiftieth of a circle and that the distance between Syene and Alexandria was 5000 stadia.

Earthpeople Book: What is a stadia?

Eratosthenes: Stadium. Stadia is the plural. It's our unit of length. One stadium is equal to about 600 Greek feet, 607 English feet, or 200 meters.

Earthpeople Book: OK. Then what did you do?

Eratosthenes: Well, the distance —5000 stadia—was equal to one fiftieth of a circle. From looking at other celestial objects, I assumed that the earth was round, so I then multiplied 5000 stadia by 50. I estimated the earth to be about 250,000 stadia. This is equal to about 46,250 of your kilometers.

Earthpeople Book: How close is this to the actual circumference of the earth?

Eratosthenes: With your advanced measurement techniques, I believe you arrived at 40,000 kilometers, or about 25,000 miles. I was only 6,250 kilometers off! Not bad at all! Why don't you try your luck at measurement?

Earthpeople Book: How?

Eratosthenes: Do the next activity in this book!

Sizing Up the Earth

In this activity you can measure the earth as did Eratosthenes, that Greek master of geography.

Materials
Globe of the earth
2 sticks, each about 10 cm long
Millimeter ruler
Small amount of plasticene (to hold the sticks)
Protractor
Bright sunshine!

Procedure
1. Determine the angle a of the shadow cast by a stick placed in the ground in a vertical position at noon.

2. Draw a line in the figure below to show where no shadow would be cast.

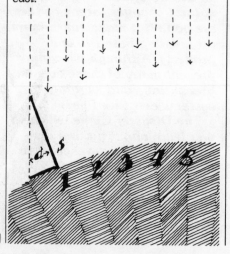

3. You should have drawn a line above position 5 on the diagram.
4. Now set up the globe and two sticks as in the diagram below.

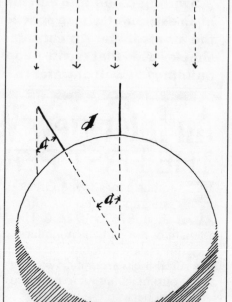

5. Measure the distance between the two sticks using a mm ruler. Measure the shadow angle at a with a protractor.
6. Use the following formula to calculate the circumference of the globe.

$$\frac{Circumference\ of\ globe}{Distance\ between\ sticks} = \frac{Angle\ of\ full\ circle}{Angle\ a}$$

Hint: Angle of full circle = 360°
7. How close is your answer to the established circumference of the globe?

Earth–It's A-changin'

How dynamic is our planet? Some changes are so subtle that you hardly notice them: A butterfly lands on a rose petal. Others tear you from a sound sleep: A tornado roars, an earthquake cracks. Here is a collection of activities guaranteed to convince the most conservative of us that some things do change. Enjoy!

1. Keep a record of phenomena over a two-week period. Make your observations at the same time each day. Here are some things to observe: air temperature, percentage of clouds in the sky, your morning disposition, phases of the moon, weather, number of kids absent in your classroom, headline in the evening newspaper.

2. Prove that some living thing in your environment changes.

3. Go outside and find evidence of a natural occurrence. (You define "natural.")

4. Find a change in your environment that is predictable. While you are doing so, look also for a change that is unpredictable.

5. Identify things that change, then move like these changes. Some examples are a caterpillar becoming a butterfly, a rock rolling down a hill, and a tree swaying in the wind.

6. Make a list of changes, such as new buildings, that have taken place in your community during the past year. Decide whether each change was good or bad for your community. Select one good and one bad change. For each one, write an editorial letter to those responsible for the change.

7. How do sounds change? Use a tape recorder to record differences among the morning, afternoon, and evening sounds where you live. Challenge your friends to a listening contest.

8. Find evidence in your environment of a good change and a bad change. Use your resources to make the bad change good.

9. What causes change? Find sets of two things in your environment, one of which is responsible for the other. A crack in a sidewalk through which a plant pokes and a shadow cast by a tree in the path of the sun are sets that come to mind.

10. Find something in the environment that is increasing in number and something that is decreasing in number. Present proof positive of both.

11. Using pictures from magazines and newspapers, create a poster that shows the earth undergoing as many changes as you can find.

Adapted from *Essence II* (Menlo Park, Calif.: Addison-Wesley, 1970), © 1970 American Geological Institute. This publication is not endorsed by the copyright holder.

Wladimir Köppen, CLIMATOLOGIST (1846–1940)

Wladimir Köppen was born in Russia and spent his youth in Crimea, where he became interested in the way climate and plant life affect each other. Köppen spent half a century as a meteorologist (weatherman) at the German Naval Observatory. There he made a series of maps of the ocean wind and continued his study of climate and vegetation. In an effort to classify the climates of the world, he invented a system based on regional varieties of plant life. His simple and very clever system divides the earth into five zones, which are subdivided according to temperature, amount of rainfall, and their effects on plant life. Because of his creative and pioneering work, Wladimir Köppen is considered the father of modern climatology (the study of climates).

The Mysterious Continent

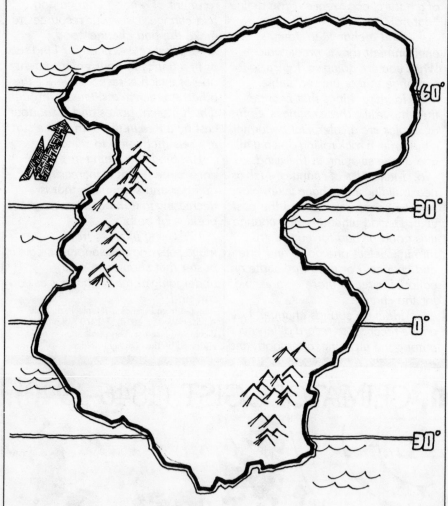

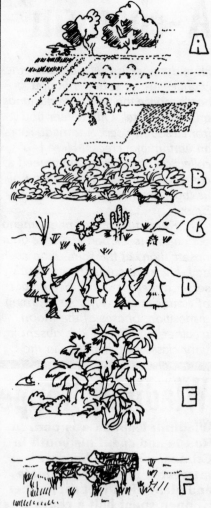

Imagine this scene: You are flying your own jet plane across the ocean. After passing through a dense fog bank, you pick up what appears to be a rather large land mass on your radar screen. Your knowledge of geography tells you that no land mass has ever been mapped in this region. You continue on and sure enough, there it is.

You decide to use your radar scanning system to make a rough map of the area. After several passes north and south, east and west, your computer prints out this map, complete with latitude, boundaries, and mountains. After a few moments of inspection, you realize that you've discovered a mysterious continent!

One of your first concerns is to study the climate of the mysterious continent. Follow these steps and see how you do.

1. In pencil, lightly sketch where you think the general boundaries of the climatic regions would be, based on temperature and moisture. Label the regions considering the following conditions: hot, warm, cold, humid, and dry.

2. Use the Super Climate Chart on page 81 to identify the locations of the six climatic types.

a. What type of vegetation would you expect to find in each zone? Make up a key for your map and key each vegetation

on the map.

b. Where are the humid and dry areas? How do these locations compare to your original sketch?

3. Using what you have learned thus far, look at the drawings and write in the letter for each drawing on your mysterious continent map in the correct climatic location. Base your decision on the type of vegetation shown in each picture, guesses you can make about the amount of precipitation, and the geographical features of the land. To check on whether your judgment of the type of climate for each drawing is correct, turn to the appendix.

Ocean Rivers

In 1769 Benjamin Franklin drew a map of the Gulf Stream that looked like the map at the right. At that time he was deputy postmaster of the American colonies and had noticed that ships sailing from England to America took as much as 2 weeks longer than ships making the return voyage. Look at the map and guess the reason for this difference. Write your guess here:

_____

Did you guess that ships traveling westward toward America sailed against the direction of the current? Naturally, their sailing time would be slower. If you did, good for you.

Oceanographers have mapped the ocean currents and have determined that currents flow in all of the ocean basins of the earth. The direction and location of currents are shown with arrows on this map. The scientific explanation of the cause of the current states that the prevailing winds in each ocean basin "drive" the ocean currents.

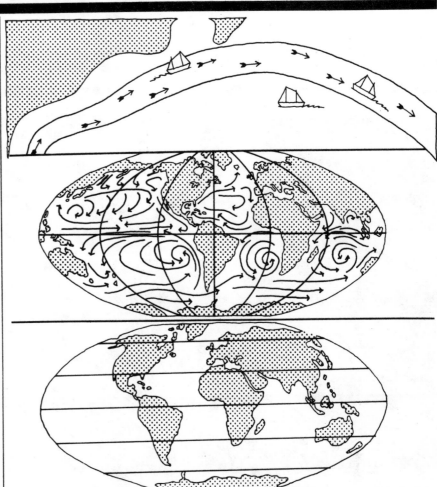

"Current" Events

1. *Prove the theory of ocean currents yourself. Use the blank map to draw in what you think are the directions of the prevailing winds in each of the ocean basins. Then check the map of winds in the appendix of the book. Do the directions of the prevailing winds match up with the ocean currents?*

2. *What path would you follow to make any of the following voyages in a ship? Mark your trip paths on the blank map. Why did you choose these paths?*

Port of Departure	Port of Arrival
Northern Africa	Florida
Japan	Southern California
Brazil	Eastern Australia

3. *Find out where these currents are located: Labrador Current, Japan Current, North Atlantic Drift, and Humboldt Current.*

4. *Currents flowing from regions near the equator toward polar regions carry warmer water and are thus called warm currents. What kind of current is the Gulf Stream?*

5. *What is a cold current?*

6. *Are the currents listed in question 3 warm or cold?*

Super Climate Chart

Type of Climate	Location on a Continent	Annual Precipitation	Type of Vegetation
Marine west coast	West coast	50–75 cm	Cone-bearing forest
Desert	Just interior from west coast	less than 25 cm	Cacti
Steppe	East of desert area	more than 25 cm	Grasses, hardy plants, cacti
Mediterranean	Southwest coast	approximately 25 cm	Evergreen shrubs
Humid subtropical	Eastern edge	75–165 cm	Heavy plant growth and forests
Humid continental	Heart of Continent to east coast	at least 75 cm	Grasses, hardwood and softwood trees

9

Places

Earthpeople are always interested in places. We make maps of places, take pictures of places, think about places to visit, and sometimes even take trips to see these places.

Earthpeople who study places to find out how they were formed are known as geologists and geographers. Geologists study the history of places and the kinds of rocks found above and below ground. They use what they learn to make maps. Geographers study the surface features of places, including their environment, natural resources, and inhabitants. Both are interested in how and why a place changes and what effects these changes have on the people who live there. These are some of the things that you will discover in this chapter. While you work in this chapter, try not to lose your place!

Window Geography

Just think of all the time you have spent sitting in a seat in a school bus or in your parents' car. Here is an activity that will pass the time as you travel from place to place. You will study how people use the land. It will help to have a friend with you to record data.

Of all the material resources we have on the earth, the most important is land. Some people believe that the way we use the land affects its future. Poor land use will probably lead to a decline in the quality of life, while proper use of the land will guard it as a good resource for many generations of earthpeople.

Window Watching

1. Do the activity as you travel in a bus, car, or train during the daytime. So, the first requirement is to find a vehicle!

2. Work in a group of three. One person will be the timer to give signals to the observers.

3. The timer should instruct the observers to make an observation every 30 seconds. The observers should be looking out opposite

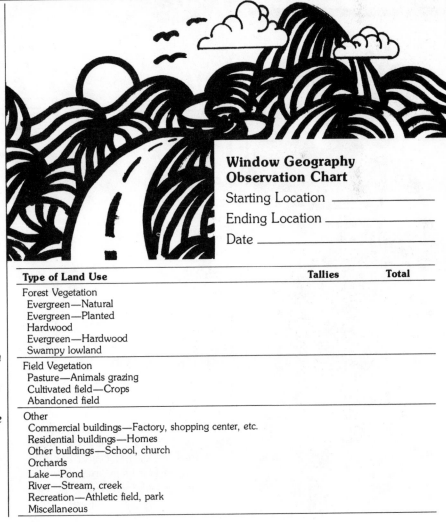

**Window Geography
Observation Chart**

Starting Location _____

Ending Location _____

Date _____

Type of Land Use	Tallies	Total
Forest Vegetation		
Evergreen—Natural		
Evergreen—Planted		
Hardwood		
Evergreen—Hardwood		
Swampy lowland		
Field Vegetation		
Pasture—Animals grazing		
Cultivated field—Crops		
Abandoned field		
Other		
Commercial buildings—Factory, shopping center, etc.		
Residential buildings—Homes		
Other buildings—School, church		
Orchards		
Lake—Pond		
River—Stream, creek		
Recreation—Athletic field, park		
Miscellaneous		

sides of the vehicle that they are traveling in.

4. At the 30 second observation points, the observers should make a tally on a chart (similar to the one on page 83) of the type of land use they observe.

5. In 1 hour this will produce 120 observations for each side of the vehicle.

6. Total the tallies in each category and subcategory.

After you have computed the totals, think about these questions.

1. What was the most common use of the land on your trip?

2. How are humans managing the land in the area through which you traveled? Did you observe any of the following: litter, pollution, beauty, or landscape improvement projects?

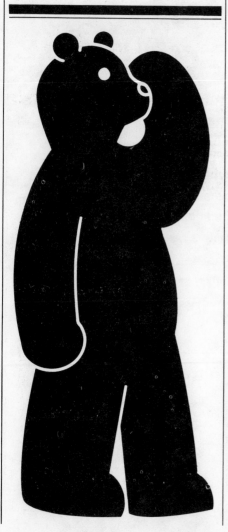

National Parks
PLACES TO VISIT

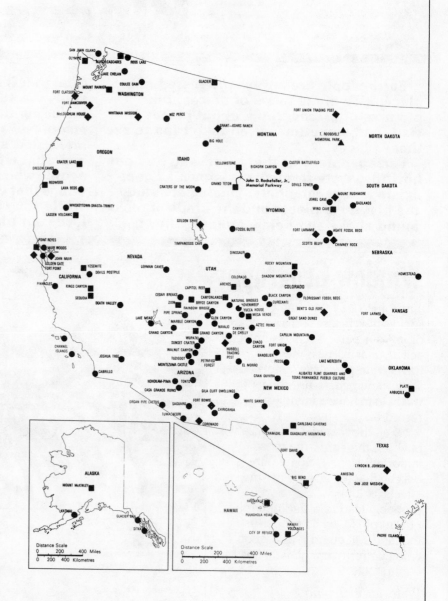

The national park system was established by the United States government in 1872. The first parkland was Yellowstone National Park. The system has grown from one park in 1872 to over three hundred parks that cover an area larger than Pennsylvania. Every state except Delaware has at least one park. The national park system includes many types of areas.

This map shows the location of all the parklands in the national park system. First, make a list of the parks that you have visited, or simply circle them on the map. After selecting the parkland you would like to visit, read through the rest of this activity.

Where to Write
If you want addresses for any of

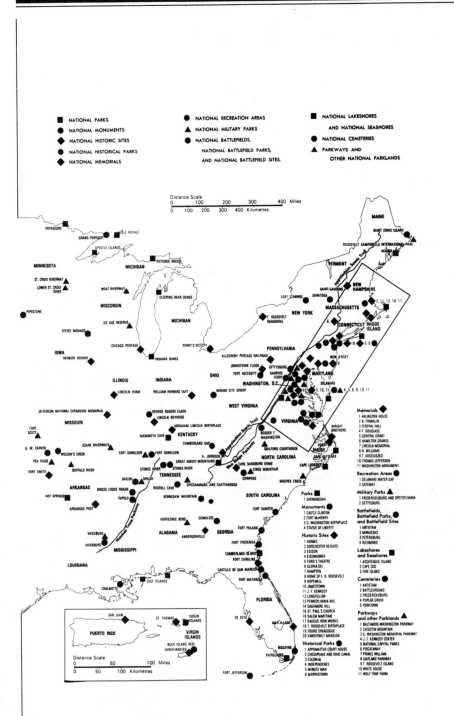

National Parks
National Monuments
National Historic Sites
National Historical Parks
National Memorials
National Recreation Areas
National Military Parks
National Battlefields, National Battlefield Parks, and National Battlefield Sites.
National Lakeshores and National Seashores
National Cemeteries
Parkways and Other National Parklands

Distance Scale
0   100   200   300   400   Miles
0   100   200   300   400   Kilometres

VOYAGEURS
GRAND PORTAGE
ISLE ROYALE
APOSTLE ISLANDS
PICTURED ROCKS
MINNESOTA
ST. CROIX RIVERWAY
LOWER ST. CROIX RIVER
PIPESTONE
WISCONSIN
WOLF RIVERWAY
SLEEPING BEAR DUNES
MICHIGAN
ICE AGE RESERVE
EFFIGY MOUNDS
IOWA
HERBERT HOOVER
CHICAGO PORTAGE
PERRY'S VICTORY
INDIANA DUNES
ILLINOIS
INDIANA
OHIO
LINCOLN HOME
WILLIAM HOWARD TAFT
MOUND CITY GROUP
JEFFERSON NATIONAL EXPANSION MEMORIAL
GEORGE ROGERS CLARK
LINCOLN BOYHOOD
MISSOURI
FORT SCOTT
ABRAHAM LINCOLN BIRTHPLACE
WEST VIRGINIA
MAMMOTH CAVE
KENTUCKY
CUMBERLAND GAP
G. W. CARVER
OZARK RIVERWAYS
WILSON'S CREEK
FORT DONELSON
FORT DONELSON
PEA RIDGE
BUFFALO RIVER
FORT SMITH
STONES RIVER
STONES RIVER
GREAT SMOKY MOUNTAINS
CARL SANDBURG HOME
KINGS MOUNTAIN
ARKANSAS
SHILOH
SHILOH
RUSSELL CAVE
CHICKAMAUGA AND CHATTANOOGA
HOT SPRINGS
PINCES CROSS ROADS
TUPELO
KENNESAW MOUNTAIN
TENNESSEE
COWPENS
SOUTH CAROLINA
MOORES CREEK
VICKSBURG
VICKSBURG
HORSESHOE BEND
OCMULGEE
FORT SUMTER
ALABAMA
ANDERSONVILLE
GEORGIA
FORT PULASKI
MISSISSIPPI
FORT FREDERICA
LOUISIANA
CUMBERLAND ISLAND
FORT CAROLINE
CASTILLO DE SAN MARCOS
CHALMETTE
GULF ISLANDS
FORT MATANZAS
FLORIDA
DE SOTO
MAR-A-LAGO
BISCAYNE
EVERGLADES
FORT JEFFERSON

MAINE
SAINT CROIX ISLAND
ROOSEVELT CAMPOBELLO INTERNATIONAL PARK
ACADIA
VERMONT
Appalachian Scenic Trail
NEW HAMPSHIRE
SAINT-GAUDENS
SARATOGA
FORT STANWIX
NEW YORK
T. ROOSEVELT INAUGURAL
MASSACHUSETTS
CONNECTICUT
RHODE ISLAND
PENNSYLVANIA
ALLEGHENY PORTAGE RAILROAD
JOHNSTOWN FLOOD
GETTYSBURG
NEW JERSEY
FORT NECESSITY
HARPERS FERRY
WASHINGTON, D.C.
MARYLAND
DELAWARE
WRIGHT BROTHERS
A. JOHNSON
Blue Ridge Parkway
VIRGINIA
BOOKER T. WASHINGTON
GUILFORD COURTHOUSE
FORD'S
RALEIGH
CAPE HATTERAS
NORTH CAROLINA
CAPE LOOKOUT
Natchez Trace Parkway

Memorials ◆
1 ARLINGTON HOUSE
2 B. FRANKLIN
3 FEDERAL HALL
4 F. DOUGLASS
5 GENERAL GRANT
6 HAMILTON GRANGE
7 LINCOLN MEMORIAL
8 R. WILLIAMS
9 T. KOSCIUSZKO
10 THOMAS JEFFERSON
11 WASHINGTON MONUMENT

Recreation Areas ●
1 DELAWARE WATER GAP
2 GATEWAY

Parks ■
1 SHENANDOAH

Monuments ●
1 CASTLE CLINTON
2 FORT McHENRY
3 G. WASHINGTON BIRTHPLACE
4 STATUE OF LIBERTY

Historic Sites ◆
1 ADAMS
2 DORCHESTER HEIGHTS
3 EDISON
4 EISENHOWER
5 FORD'S THEATRE
6 GLORIA DEI
7 HAMPTON
8 HOME OF F. D. ROOSEVELT
9 HOPEWELL
10 JAMESTOWN
11 J. F. KENNEDY
12 LONGFELLOW
13 PENNSYLVANIA AVE.
14 SAGAMORE HILL
15 ST. PAUL'S CHURCH
16 SALEM MARITIME
17 SAUGUS IRON WORKS
18 T. ROOSEVELT BIRTHPLACE
19 TOURO SYNAGOGUE
20 VANDERBILT MANSION

Historical Parks ◆
1 APPOMATTOX COURT HOUSE
2 CHESAPEAKE AND OHIO CANAL
3 COLONIAL
4 INDEPENDENCE
5 MINUTE MAN
6 MORRISTOWN

Military Parks ●
1 FREDERICKSBURG AND SPOTSYLVANIA
2 GETTYSBURG

Battlefields, Battlefield Parks, and Battlefield Sites ●
1 ANTIETAM
2 MANASSAS
3 PETERSBURG
4 RICHMOND

Lakeshores and Seashores ■
1 ASSATEAGUE ISLAND
2 CAPE COD
3 FIRE ISLAND

Cemeteries ●
1 ANTIETAM
2 BATTLEGROUND
3 FREDERICKSBURG
4 POPLAR GROVE
5 YORKTOWN

Parkways and other Parklands ▲
1 BALTIMORE-WASHINGTON PARKWAY
2 CATOCTIN MOUNTAIN
3 G. WASHINGTON MEMORIAL PARKWAY
4 J. F. KENNEDY CENTER
5 NATIONAL CAPITAL PARKS
6 PISCATAWAY
7 PRINCE WILLIAM
8 SUITLAND PARKWAY
9 T. ROOSEVELT ISLAND
10 WHITE HOUSE
11 WOLF TRAP FARM

SAN JUAN
ST. THOMAS
VIRGIN ISLANDS
PUERTO RICO
VIRGIN ISLANDS
BUCK ISLAND REEF
CHRISTIANSTED

Distance Scale
0   50   100   Miles
0   50   100   Kilometres

Activity	What to Do
Categ-o-Riddles	*Select an area of the parkland and classify everything in it as animal, vegetable, or mineral.*
System Ties	*Find ten or more systems in the parkland. Then find at least one complete system within each of these.*
Joyspace	*Find joy in the parkland. If you find places that seem not to have joy, try to make some.*
Predator-Prey	*Find out who or what in the park are predators and which ones are prey.*
Aging	*Find the youngest and oldest thing in the park.*
Lookout	*Go to the best lookout spot in the park. What kinds of things can you see?*
Communicate	*Go outside and find a person or persons willing to communicate with you.*
Map-around	*Use a park map to travel around the park.*
Mapping	*Map the places in the park in which you feel most and least comfortable.*

the national parks write to the Chief, Branch of General Inquiries, Office of Information, National Park Service, Department of the Interior, Washington, DC 20240.

What to Bring
Camera
Comfortable sneakers
Canteen with your favorite fruit punch
Munchies (we suggest a mixture of raisins, mandarins, and dry-roasted peanuts)
Bandages
Plenty of energy

What to Do
Here is a list of activities to do while visiting a parkland. You will have to determine which activity is suitable to the parkland you visit.

Indoor & Outdoor

Follow the Leader on a Map

You need
Wall map
Ruler or pointer

Here's How to Play

One player is the leader. This person gives directions to another player, who moves a ruler or pointer on the map to where the leader directs. The leader may use only words.

In one game, the player is never allowed to lift the pointer off the map.

In another game, someone thinks of a specific location on the map, writes it down, and hides it from the leader and the rest of the players. The leader gives different directions to each player in turn. The player who ends up closest to the hidden location is the next leader.

Looking at Different Maps

You need
Collection of different maps: road maps, survey maps, local maps, world maps, weather maps, moon maps

Here's How to Play

Each group studies a different map. If you have a local map, find the location of your house, your school, the nearest church, the fire station, and the library.

What does each color on the map mean? What do the dots and solid lines mean? You may want to keep notes of what you find.

After you have studied one map for a while, you can be considered the expert on your map.

Exchange your map with another group. Look at the second map.

Do the colors, lines, and symbols have the same meaning on this map as they did on the first one? Which things are the same and which are different on the two maps?

Check back with the original map readers. Compare your notes with theirs. Did you discover the same things? Compare the two maps (or more if you have more groups). Which map gives the most information? What would you use each map for?

Following Your Way Around the Room

You need
Pencils
Index cards

Here's How to Play

Pick two points in the room that are at least 15 ft. (about 5 m) apart. You can call them A and B. Do not tell your partner where they are. Make sure that there are things like desks and chairs between A and B.

Write directions or draw a map to guide your partner to A and from A to B without banging into any furniture. Tell your partner where A is if a clue is necessary. Then blindfold yourself and have your partner give you the directions aloud. Were you able to find your way from A to B?

Twenty Questions on a Map

You need
Large map

Here's How to Play

One person, the leader, thinks of a place on the map. The rest of the group asks questions, such as, Is it west of the Mississippi? Does it have a large river running through it? Is it full of large cities? Do they grow a lot of corn there? Was Abe Lincoln born there? Does it have the highest mountain in the United States?

Everyone who wants to should have a chance to be a leader.

Mapping the Room

You need
Drawing materials

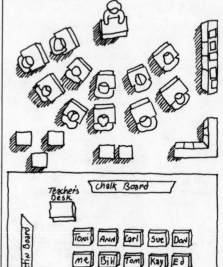

Here's How to Play

The pictures show some maps that other students have made of their classrooms. Can you imagine what these classrooms look like? Are there things you would like to know that you can't find out from the maps?

Make a map of your classroom. You'll have to decide where things go, how big things should be, where you'll stand when you draw the map, and other details, such as whether or not to show the lights on the ceiling. When you've finished, see whether you can use your map to help someone find an object in the room.

Path Puzzles

You need
Index cards
Paper
Pencils

Mapping Games

Here's How to Play

Have your partner draw a path with four moves, starting in a place where there is a lot of room. Can you predict, before you walk it out, where the path will end? Try it and see. Try one with five moves, six moves. For how long a path can you predict the end correctly?

On an index card, draw a path that, when you walk it out, gets you back to where you started in four moves, in five moves.

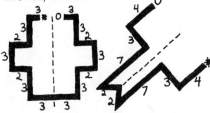

These are pictures of "mirror paths." Put a mirror on the dotted line and look in the mirror. When you take the mirror away, your path should look the same as it did when the mirror was still there.

Try writing word directions for a mirror path.

Hide and Seek With a Compass

You need
Object to hide
Directional compass

Here's How to Play

One person hides an object and gives the *fewest* possible compass directions to the hiding place. No pointing or giving landmarks as clues is allowed. Everyone should have a turn to hide the object and give directions.

Finding Your Way Around Outdoors

You need
Directional compass
Pencils
Index cards

Here's How to Play

Pick three places in the school-yard that are far apart and call them A, B, and C. Write how to get from A to B to C using distances and compass headings.

Give the same written directions to several people. Do they all end up in the same place? Try giving directions, using only landmarks. Try to give useful directions without giving distances.

Mapping Your Way Home on Foot

You need
Drawing materials

Here's How to Play

Draw a map showing the easiest way to get home from school on foot. Show all the shortcuts you usually take. Show all the landmarks a stranger would have to know about to get to your house in the shortest time. Time how long it takes you and put that on your map, too.

Give your map to someone and see whether he or she can follow the route.

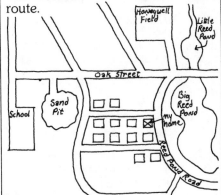

Mapping Your Way From School to Home

You need
Drawing materials
Commercial maps

Here's How to Play

Draw a map showing how you would go home from school if you were traveling

1. By helicopter
2. Along telephone wires
3. On a bike
4. In a car
5. By boat

Try as many of these as you like. How do your maps differ from one another? What landmarks are important in each case? What would a stranger need to know to follow these routes?

Try one of your maps out on someone else. Does it work? Can your friend read your map or, better yet, follow it?

Feeling Map

You need
Drawing materials
Map from Mapping Your Way
  Home on Foot

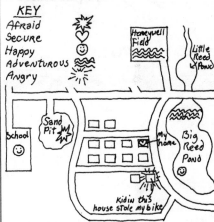

Here's How to Play

Use the map you prepared earlier. Walk around your neighborhood, trying as you do to describe your feelings at different places. You might consider feelings like happy, afraid, adventurous, angry, and secure. Indicate your feelings on the appropriate places on your map. Color the map using a key for each feeling. Compare your map with others.

How to Use a Map to See

What do airline pilots, geologists, foresters, rangers, mountaineers, boy and girl scouts, campers, and birds have in common? Come on, try harder. Did we hear you say their need for map reading? Even if you did say this, you may still be wondering what birds have in common with all the others. Well, it's this: the map you see below is a bird's-eye view of the land, a detailed view that shows distance to scale as well as elevation above sea level. To give you an idea of what a map can represent, look at these three drawings.

Each of the lines on the map is a contour line. Contour lines connect points on the earth's surface that have the same elevation or depth. For example, if you were to get on the 100 ft. contour line and walk around on it, you would remain at the same level. If you crossed the line and walked toward the 200 ft. contour line, you would walk uphill. In this activity, you will learn how to use a topographic map and have some fun as well. The map you are going to use is of Estes Park, Colorado, located at over 7000 ft. above sea level. Take a minute to glance at the map of the area on page 90.

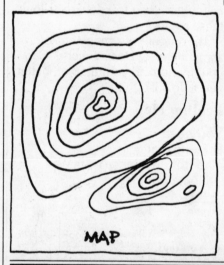

MAP

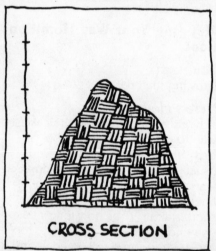

CROSS SECTION

ACTUAL

Maps and Symbols

To get you acquainted with Estes Park, find a location for each of the following features. Use the grid system shown on the map to indicate the location.

Feature	Symbol	Location
Church	⛪	E4
Building (dwelling)		
Oil tank		
Lake		
Secondary highway		
Open pit (gravel)		
Trail		
Power plant		

Estes Park Puzzlers

1. What is the highest mountain on the map and where is it located?

2. What is the primary economy of Estes Park?

3. Why aren't there many roads and buildings in the northern part of the map?

4. Find The Twin Owls on the map. Which side has the steeper slope? How do you know?

5. In what direction does the water in Black Canyon Creek flow?

Can you prove this? (Hint: Where does the creek end?)

Picture Geology

On the map on page 90, locate an area for each of the photographs shown here. Use the grid system.

A—Power Plant

B—Estes Park

C—Rocky Mountains

D—Camping in the Mountains

E—Go Climb a Rock

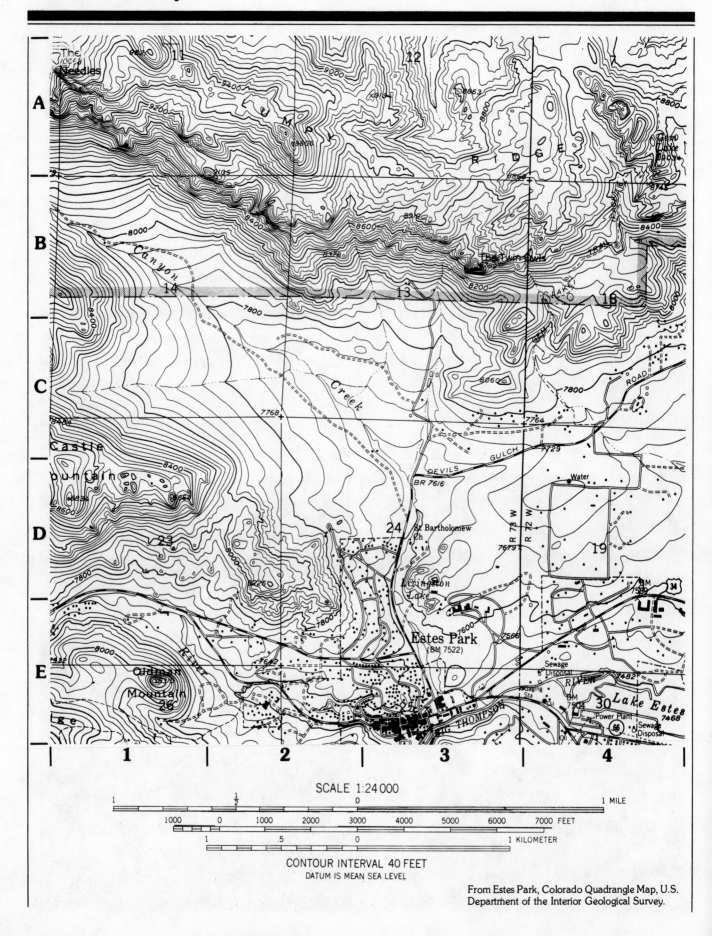

SCALE 1:24 000

CONTOUR INTERVAL 40 FEET
DATUM IS MEAN SEA LEVEL

From Estes Park, Colorado Quadrangle Map, U.S.
Department of the Interior Geological Survey.

Mystery Map

You have just anchored your sailboat off the coast of an uncharted island in the Pacific Ocean. After rowing ashore, your explorations lead you to a cave littered with human skeletons. Among the skeletons you find a large book. You carefully examine the old book and discover it is a ship's log. With much effort, you barely make out the last entry.

Follow the directions carefully and place a small x where you think the gold is hidden. Good luck!

Thank you, David Philler, for sharing this activity with us.

Ship's Log: H.M.S. Northampton

the Seventh day of October,
Sixteen Hundred and Ninety Four

I doubt that I shall survive the day. the last of my crew fell victim to the fever at sunrise. those of us who were able to swim to shore amid the sharks and pounding surf have been surviving on little or no food for twenty-three days. Perhaps we could have made it had it not been for the dreaded and disease-carrying mosquitoes. Now I am the only one left, and I cannot last but a few more hours.

On Sunday, Weston and I took what gold we had salvaged from the wrecked ship and hid it on the island. the gold can do me no good, so I bequeath to the finder of this log all the wealth that it brings... if you can find it.

Here are the directions. Follow them with care: Begin at the wreck of the Northampton. Travel east until you reach a stream. Walk upstream until you reach an elevation of 160 ft. then walk north until you are on top of the highest mountain on the island. Now travel 6 mi. east. Climb to the top of the closest mountain. Go to the nearest water. Hike 9 mi. south. Go about 3 mi. southwest until you find more water. Travel north until you get to an elevation of 240 ft. Turn east until you reach an elevation of 80 ft. Walk due north until you reach an elevation of 20 ft. You have found gold!

In Service of the Queen
Captain James Teppington

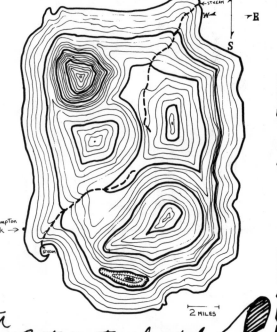

N
STREAM
W
E
S

Northampton Wreck →

STREAM

2 MILES

Contour interval: 20 feet

10

Resources

Our planet is a source of food and water for over 4 billion humans and many billions of plants and animals. In the 1960s humans ventured into space and looked back to see the planet earth. This view of the earth and its resources as a blue and white spinning globe marked the beginning of a new era for humans. In many ways our planet earth is an "earthship" on a journey through space, and with us are all the resources that we will ever have.

Some people consider the earthship idea a gloomy one. But think about all the resources we have with us on our journey. You will probably agree that important resources to humans and other forms of life include water, air, soil, fuels, and other sources of energy. Missing from the list is the most important resource on the planet earth. Can you resourceful people guess what we are thinking about? Give up? OK. The most important resource is . . .

. . . creative people! Earthpeople are equipped with the resources to create ideas, invent tools, write books, climb mountains, solve problems, run distances at greater and greater speeds, explore new horizons of the universe, fight for freedom, uncover new energy sources, adapt to a great variety of environments, dream, hope, love, and discover other untapped resources within themselves. All of these, and many, many more, are uniquely human qualities and are the most important resources on our earthship. Throughout this book we have described humans who have used their creativity in a variety of ways as they reached for knowledge and tried to help humankind. Creative people come in all sizes and shapes, sexes, colors, and religions. As you work with *Earthpeople,* and particularly with this chapter on resources, try to remember that human creativity is one of the most important resources we have.

Local Resources Study

Your own community is one place where you can study the earth's resources. Each community has problems unique to its own location, caused by such factors as climate, income, local laws and regulations, differences among people, the age of the town, and the attitude of its people toward the environment.

Following is a list of survey questions that you may find useful in starting a study of your community's resources. You might get several of your friends to agree to help you. Organize your survey so that you each contribute to the whole study.

Plan on presenting comments about each survey question you answer. Check the telephone book for phone numbers and addresses of ecology-minded groups such as the Sierra Club. If you get an older person interested in your project, you could find this person to be a source of both wisdom and transportation.

Operation Resource

1. Are there laws about the use of sprays for crops or for mosquito control?

2. Where are the pollution control districts? Soil conservation districts?

3. Are there rat control programs? What poisons are used?

4. Is there a sewage treatment system? How good is it? How can your city get it?

5. Are there health services available for the poor? Is there a special health center for women?

6. Are people going hungry? Why?

7. Is there enough bus or other mass transit service?

8. Are there enough benches around town?

9. Are there enough neighborhood miniparks?

10. Does the city have free trees

for citizens to plant in parking strips? Which areas need trees? Can students plant trees and create new miniparks?

11. Does the city have a recycling program for glass or metal?

12. Are there bicycle paths?

13. Are environmental bulletin boards available?

14. Does the library have a comprehensive section on ecology?

15. Are there stores that sell health foods?

16. Are there special activities for senior citizens?

17. Are there any city ordinances that stand in the way of ecological reform that should be amended or repealed? (Three South San Francisco students got their city to pass an ordinance banning non-returnable bottles!)

18. Does your city have malls or shopping centers?

19. Take a look at the city's master plan to find out about the zoning laws. Do they cover all the needs of the people, not just business and housing needs?

20. Are there vacant lots that could become temporary or permanent parks?

21. Are there traffic islands of asphalt or cement that could be planted with shrubbery or flowers?

22. Do city offices sell their waste paper for recycling or do they just throw it out?

23. Do students ever help the community by painting park benches, planting replacement turf, cleaning up, or growing food for the poor?

24. Does the land around the community absorb and hold enough rainfall for the water supply? Does the land need new forests or other protection to maintain its water-

collecting ability?

25. Does your community allow open-dump fires? Why? How could this practice be stopped?

26. What are the local air and water pollution laws and ordinances? Are they being properly enforced? Is your local U.S. attorney enforcing the 1889 Refuse Act?

27. What are the community's billboard advertising practices? Can they be improved?

28. Are superhighways being planned in your area? Will their "right-of-way" destroy neighborhoods or natural lands?

29. Does your city or state offer bounties for certain animals and birds?

30. How much marshland exists in your community and state? Is it being protected?

Woodmongers

The energy crisis that we all have lived with for the last few years is not new. Here is a statement written in 1644 by Gerrard Winstanley that was part of *A Declaration From the Poor Oppressed People of England:*

So then, we declare unto you that do intend to cut our common woods and trees, that you shall not do it; unless . . . the poor oppressed that live thereabouts may take it and employ it for their public use. Therefore take notice, we have demanded it in the name of the commons of England and of all the nations of the world, it being the righteous freedom of creation.

Likewise we declare to you that have begun to cut down our common woods and trees, and to fell and carry away the same for your private use, that you shall forbear and go no farther, hoping that none that are friends to the commonwealth of England will endeavour to buy any of those common trees and woods of any of

those lords or manors (so called) who have, by the murdering and cheating law of the sword, stolen the land from younger brothers, who have by the law of creation a standing portion in the land, as well and equal with others. Therefore we hope all woodmongers will disown all such private merchandise, as being a robbing of the poor oppressed.

Taking an Energetic Stand

1. In 1644 the British government intervened in what it recognized as an energy crisis. Do you think governments should do this and thus regulate the use of energy?

2. Some people think that the primary cause of energy crises is the unthinking exploitation of our natural resources. What do you think of this?

3. What alternative sources of fuel would have been available to people in England in 1644? Why didn't they use them?

Re-source Magazines on Energy

Alternative Sources of Energy, Route 2, Box 90-A, Milack, MN.
The Mother Earth News, P.O. Box 70, Henderson, NC 28739.

The Nuclear Power Resource

The use of nuclear fuels as a source of power is a controversial issue. Many electric power companies are building nuclear power generators to replace oil, coal, or gas power plants. There are sixteen operable nuclear power plants in the United States, fifty-four being built, and thirty-five planned (reactors ordered). Eight more plants have been announced for which reactors have not been ordered. Most of these plants are east of the Mississippi.

Research: A Radio-Activity

1. People have different opinions about our investment in the development of nuclear plants. Research some pros and cons and take your own stand.

2. What are the effects of radioactivity on our health?

3. How did the dropping of the atomic bombs on Japan affect the people and the environment?

4. The time it takes half the atoms in radioactive material to decay is its half life. The half life of the radioactive fuels and the wastes from power plants is many thousands of years. What problems could arise if waste material was buried?

5. There are other alternative energy sources to nuclear energy. The following chart lists some alternatives. Explore the advantages and disadvantages of each alternative. We have included several other categories in the chart to help you with your decisions.

Alternative Energy Analysis Chart

Energy Source	Duration of Supply	Cost of Development	Cost of Utilization	Location of Source	Type and Extent of Pollution Entailed in Use	Advantages	Disadvantages
Geothermal energy							
Nuclear energy							
Shale oil							
Solar energy							
Wind and water power							

The Dowsers

Dowsers find water beneath the ground. They walk over the ground holding a forked stick called a divining rod in front of them. If a dowser feels vibrations through the stick, that spot on the ground is marked.

Dowsing is an ancient craft that most people relegate to the realm of magic, witchcraft, or alchemy (a medieval form of chemistry with magical associations that sought to change baser elements to gold). Witch doctors—dowsers included—gave way to science and technology, but some people are still interested in these supernatural powers. We have rainmakers who sometimes succeed, witch doctors, and faith healers. In some cultures these persons are more effective than scientifically trained persons, probably because people

believe in them. Farmers have always wanted to know where to dig wells that would hit water, so they called upon the dowsers, whose ability to find the "irresistible force" led them to water.

Does it work? Well, why don't you try your hand at dowsing? You'll need to find a forked stick, or you can make one from a coat hanger. Just follow the directions on page 97. Don't be an old stick-in-the-mud.

One way to test the theory of dowsing is to map an area by sketching in where you think water pipes might be located beneath the surface. The school grounds or your home will do. Go outside and use your dowsing rod. Pass back and forth over a small area. Each

time you pick up "irresistible vibrations," indicate this point as the location of water. Check your map or plans for the buildings that show the location of water pipes.

We do not want to rule dowsers out. Many reputable scientists are presently studying human behaviors that years ago were considered nonsense. Dr. Stanley Krippner, a psychologist, is studying faith healers in several different cultures. Acupuncture, a Chinese surgical operation that relieves pain through needles pushed into the body, is becoming more common in the United States. Some universities have research projects under way on extrasensory perception, and physicists have developed models or theories to explain ESP. Perhaps all these are resources that our earthship should be monitoring.

Realms for Research
1. Rainmaking
2. Unexplained phenomena
3. Alchemy
4. Magic
5. Dreams
6. The occult

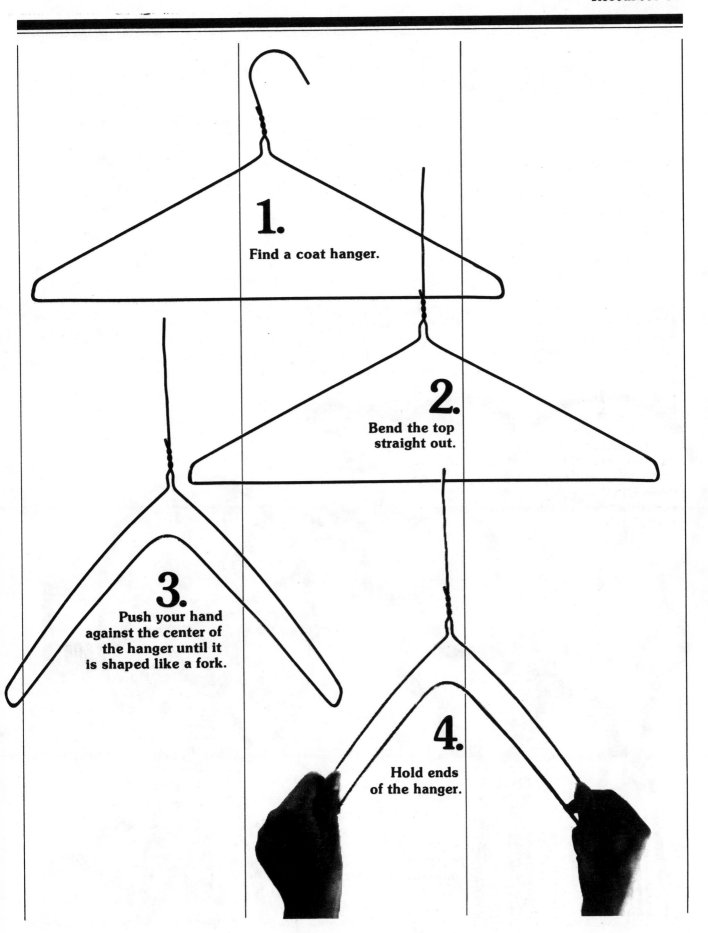

1.

Find a coat hanger.

2.

Bend the top
straight out.

3.

Push your hand
against the center of
the hanger until it
is shaped like a fork.

4.

Hold ends
of the hanger.

Searching for Soft Technologies

Hard Technology—study of the practical or industrial arts and sciences; utilization of such knowledge; knowledge and means applied to make the products that a society wants or needs.

Soft Technology—study of methods that are gentle on surroundings; response to the environment, incorporating and nurturing it.

After reading these two definitions, can you guess which technology the drawings below represent? Circle the word "hard" or "soft" for each drawing. How did you do? Did you circle "hard" for the first one and "soft" for the second?

Hard technology provides goods to people through methods that keep costs low. This usually leads to expansion, which leads to the improper use of our land and natural resources.

Soft technology's first concern is with people. Its emphasis on many small, perhaps individually owned, units to provide the same services to people is more ecological. Smaller units tend to keep the natural environment intact and provide

more people with work.

You might be thinking that soft technology does not have hardware —mechanical, magnetic, and electronic design and components. Not so. Hardware is just as important to soft as to hard technology. The difference is in its integration with the *environment*. This activity is designed to acquaint you with the concept of soft technology. You'll use your fingers (to check the yellow pages of your phone book for the topics listed), your feet (to visit a local book store or library), and perhaps an older

HARD
SOFT

HARD
SOFT

friend (to drive you to soft technology places). You might also visit hard technology places to see how they are changing to more ecological approaches.

Some Soft Technologies to Make a Dent In
1. Wood—a renewable resource
2. Water—water power plants, water wheels, hydraulic pumps
3. Wind—windmills, wind plants, wind generators, kites
4. Solar—solar heaters, solar collectors, reflector cookers, solar ovens, solar water heaters
5. Methane (swamp or bio-gas) —bio-gas plants, methane generators, anaerobic processes

Soft Topics for Hard Research
1. *What soft technology companies exist in your community?*
2. *How can a home be converted to a solar-powered house?*
3. *What places in the United States would be suitable for wind power?*
4. *Many space satellites are powered by solar generators. How do they work?*

Soft Technology Sources: Books, People, Places

Some Books
Brand, Stewart, ed. *Whole Earth Epilog.* Baltimore: Penguin Books, 1974.
Chesterman, John, et al. *An Index of Possibilities: Energy and Power.* New York: Random House, Pantheon Books, 1974.
Fuller, Buckminster. *Operating Manual for Spaceship Earth.* New York: Pocket Books, 1969.
Merrill, Richard, et al., eds. *Energy Primer.* Menlo Park, Calif.: Portola Institute, 1975.
The Mother Earth News staff. *Handbook of Homemade Power.* New York: Bantam Books, 1974.
Szczelkun, Stefan A. *Survival Scrapbook 3: Energy.* New York: Schocken Books, 1974.
The (Updated) Last Whole Earth Catalog. Baltimore: Penguin Books 1975.

Some People
Buckminster Fuller
Gregory Bateson
Rachel Carson
Stewart Brand

Some Places
Integrated Living Systems, Star Route 103, Tijeras, NM 87059.
Low Impact Technology Group, 73 Molesworth Street, Wadebridge, Cornwall, England.
The New Alchemy Institute, Box 432, Woods Hole, MA 02543.
Ouroboros Project (working toward an energy-conserving urban dwelling), University of Minnesota, School of Architecture, Minneapolis, MN 55455.

A Man Who Believed That Small Is Beautiful

E. F. Schumacher was an English economist. He was a Rhodes scholar in economics, economics advisor to the British Control Commission in postwar Germany, head of planning at the British Coal Board for 20 years. But more interesting than these are the following facts about this man. He was

1. President of the Soil Association, one of Britain's oldest organic farming organizations
2. Founder and chairman of the Intermediate Technology Development Group, which specializes in tailoring tools, small-scale machines, and methods of production to the needs of developing countries
3. Sponsor of the Fourth World Movement, a British-based organization for decentralization
4. Student of Gandhi, nonviolence, and ecology.

Schumacher believed that we need to change our attitudes, shifting our stance on economics to a people-oriented position. He felt that Western (U.S. and European) economics has encouraged an attitude toward our resources that is wasteful and nonecological, an attitude that is the major cause of the energy crisis. Schumacher looked to technology and science for methods and equipment that are cheap enough to be widely available, can be used on a small scale, and fit in with the human need for creativity. Nonviolence and a harmonious relationship with nature will sprout from these productive seeds. *Small is beautiful.*

1. *If these ideas are of interest to you, you might want to write for information to Intermediate Technology Development Group, 9 King Street, Covent Garden, London WC2, England.*
2. *How do you think large corporations would receive Schumacher's ideas?*
3. *Write to your senator or congressperson for an opinion about energy conservation bills.*

11

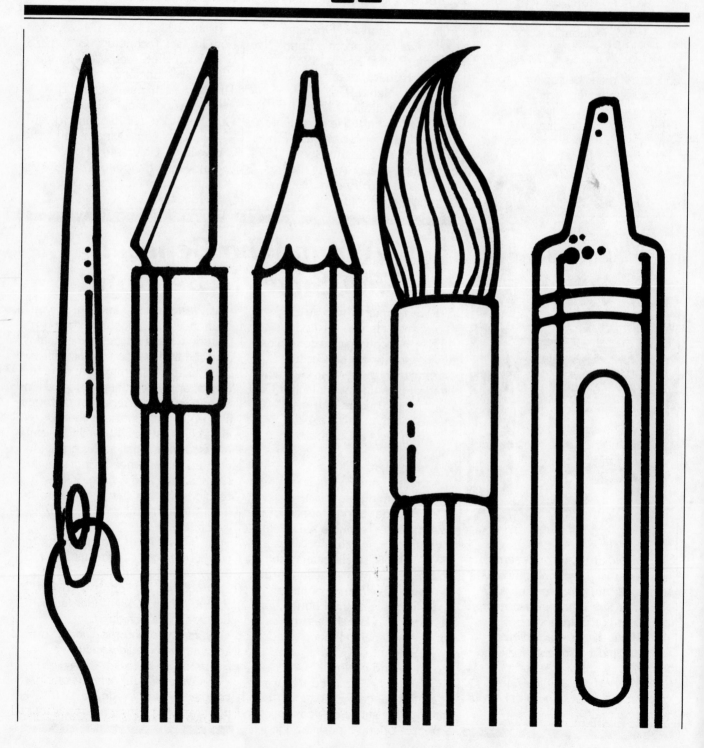

Crafts and Arts

Earthpeople handiwork is a clue to their culture. Their crafted objects reflect the kinds of available materials, the artistry of the people, and their standards of beauty. By trying some crafting on your own, you can become aware of thoughts, feelings, and their expression in different cultures. You'll be expressing yourself as someone from another culture would.

In this chapter you'll find directions for making some things that you've heard of and some that you may never have heard of. Have you ever made a dashiki, a piñata, or a vinta? You'll find out how to make all these and more. Read on and discover how to be crafty.

AFRICA

A Dashing Dashiki

A dashiki is a loose-fitting African shirt. You can make one for yourself quite easily. Make a pattern, cut it out, etc. Or should we say, "And sew on"?

Materials for the Pattern
Sheet of butcher paper, or any wrapping paper as wide as your shoulders and 5 ft. long
Scissors
Pencil

Pattern Procedure
1. Put the wrapping paper on the floor.
2. Cut out a hole in the center of the paper that is big enough for your head to fit through.
3. Put the paper pattern over your head and have a partner cut the pattern to fall somewhere between your hips and knees.

Materials for the Dashiki
Cloth the size of your pattern
Scissors
Needle and thread

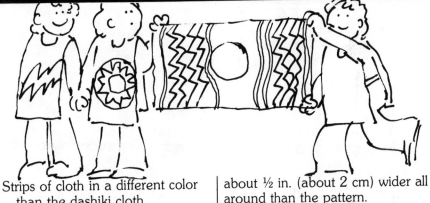

Strips of cloth in a different color than the dashiki cloth

Dashiki Directions
1. Put the pattern on your cloth.
2. Trace the pattern on the cloth so that the tracing on the cloth is about ½ in. (about 2 cm) wider all around than the pattern.
Now cut the cloth out.
3. Fold over that extra ½ in. on each side and sew these flaps to give the edges of the cloth a finished look.

Time for the Ties
1. Using the strips of cloth, cut out four pieces of the same color that are 8 in. (20 cm) long and 2 in. (5 cm) wide.
2. Fold these lengthwise and sew them each along its edge.
3. Sew one tie to each side of the dashiki where your waist would be.

Dashiki Decoration
You may wish to decorate your dashiki by sewing on pieces of colored cloth in animal shapes, geometric shapes, or other design shapes.

AFRICA
Sculpture

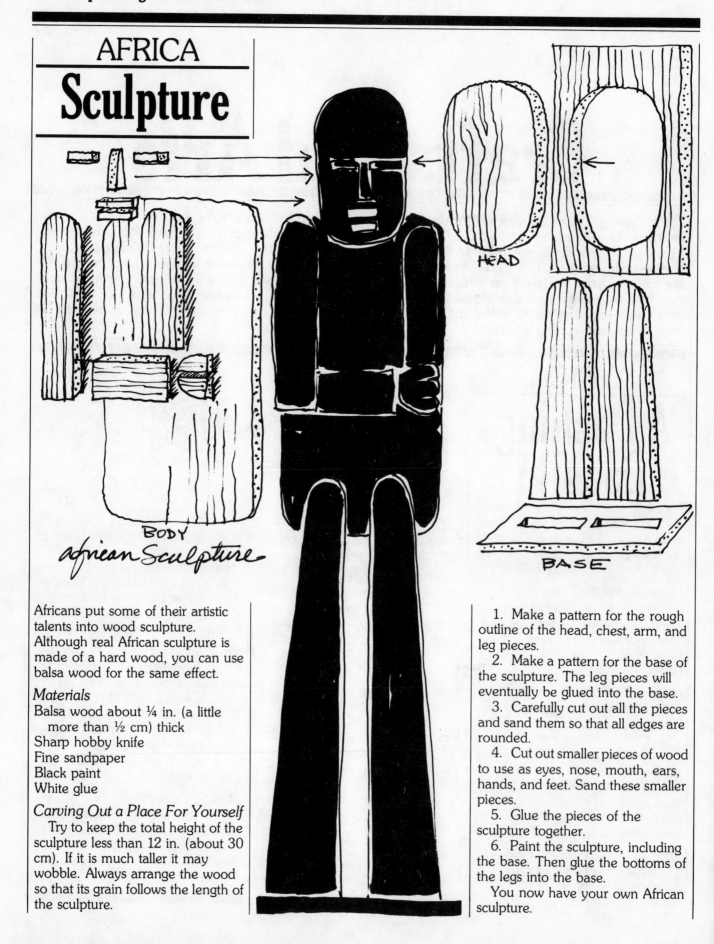

african Sculpture

BODY

HEAD

BASE

Africans put some of their artistic talents into wood sculpture. Although real African sculpture is made of a hard wood, you can use balsa wood for the same effect.

Materials
Balsa wood about ¼ in. (a little
  more than ½ cm) thick
Sharp hobby knife
Fine sandpaper
Black paint
White glue

Carving Out a Place For Yourself
  Try to keep the total height of the sculpture less than 12 in. (about 30 cm). If it is much taller it may wobble. Always arrange the wood so that its grain follows the length of the sculpture.

  1. Make a pattern for the rough outline of the head, chest, arm, and leg pieces.
  2. Make a pattern for the base of the sculpture. The leg pieces will eventually be glued into the base.
  3. Carefully cut out all the pieces and sand them so that all edges are rounded.
  4. Cut out smaller pieces of wood to use as eyes, nose, mouth, ears, hands, and feet. Sand these smaller pieces.
  5. Glue the pieces of the sculpture together.
  6. Paint the sculpture, including the base. Then glue the bottoms of the legs into the base.
  You now have your own African sculpture.

AFRICA
Tribal Masks

Many African tribes still make beautiful masks that they use as part of their religious ceremonies. This activity will show you how to make models of African masks for yourself or for others. Real African masks are carved from large pieces of wood. You will make a miniature mask of small pieces of wood glued together.

Materials
Balsa wood of different thicknesses, pieces of cardboard, or old scraps of leather
Sharp hobby knife
White glue
Fine sandpaper
Screw eye
Pieces of fabric, colored paper, and yarn
Several feet of string (less than a meter)
Paints or stain

Making Your Mask
1. Trace a pattern for the basic shape of the mask on a piece of balsa wood, cardboard, or leather.
2. Cut it out using the hobby knife. Be very careful; don't cut yourself!
3. Cut out smaller pieces for the eyes, mouth, nose, and forehead.
4. Glue the smaller pieces onto the larger one.
5. Put a screw eye into the top of the mask.
6. Sand the mask if it is made of wood.
7. Paint or stain the mask.
8. Add pieces of yarn or paper as details for the mask.
9. Loop a string to the screw eye. You now have your own pendant.

You can make larger African masks to use as wall decorations, or you can mount an assortment of miniature masks on a piece of board covered with fabric.

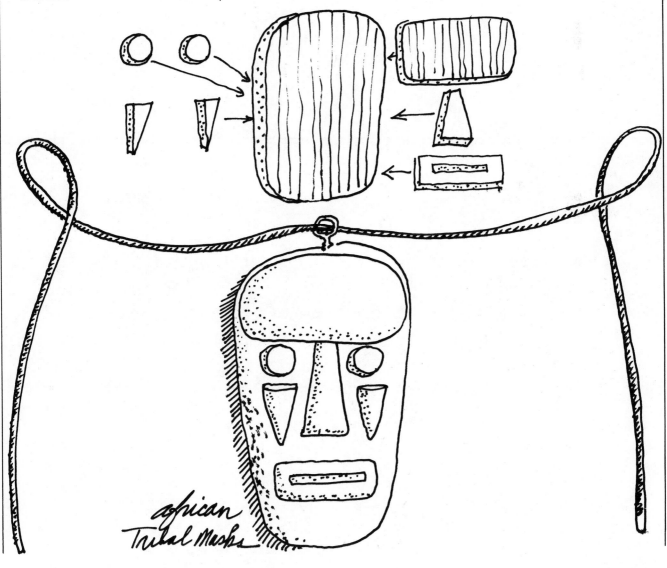

African
Tribal Masks

COSTA RICA

A Model Oxcart

In Costa Rica, a country in Central America, some farmers use oxcarts to bring fruits, vegetables, and small animals to market. Costa Ricans like to decorate their oxcarts with fancy designs.

Here is a plan you can use to make a model of a Costa Rican oxcart.

Materials

Small box about 10 cm × 15 cm × 5 cm (about 4 in. × 6 in. × 2 in.)
Thin cardboard
Brass paper fastener
Round pencil or wooden rod 1 cm (less than ½ in.) thick
White glue or paper cement
Tempera or watercolor paints
Scissors

"Operation Oxcart"

1. Cut eight posts from cardboard for the sides of the cart.

2. The tongue is that part of the cart to which the ox is harnessed. Make a cardboard tongue and connect it to the cart with the paper fastener.

3. Cut two circles from the cardboard for wheels.

4. Make a small hole through the wheels and the cart.

5. Push the pencil or rod through all the holes.

6. Cut out another piece of cardboard for a seat. Glue it in place.

7. Paint the cart and wheels, using the designs shown. The center of the wheels should be yellow. Red, blue, and black are used for the other designs.

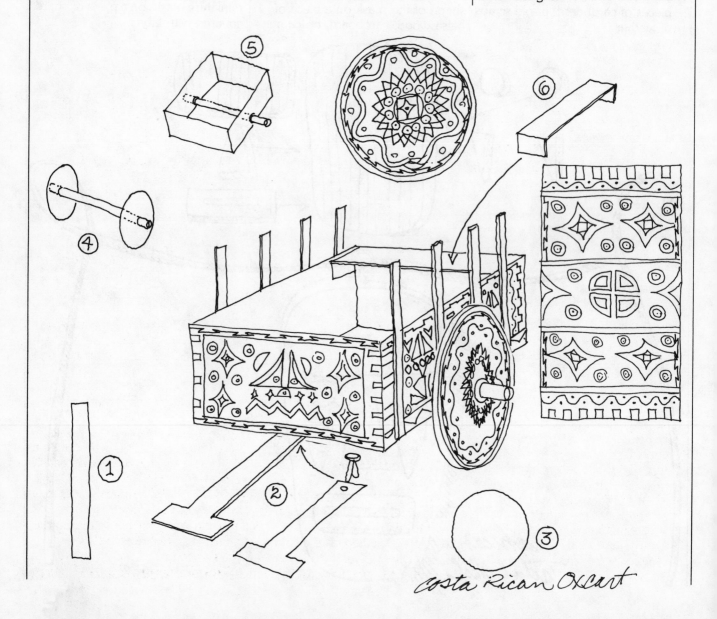

Costa Rican Oxcart

"Stained Glass" Window

EUROPE AND THE UNITED STATES

Over the centuries, men and women have shared their religious beliefs through art, music, and dance. The creation of beautiful windows put together with pieces of colored glass is one such example of artistry. The ruins of ancient churches, cathedrals, and synagogues all provide us with evidence that the use of colored glass in windows dates back thousands of years. In recent years, well-known artists such as Matisse, Chagall, and Picasso have expressed themselves using stained glass.

Perhaps you've seen stained glass windows yourself. Did you notice that strips of lead hold each piece of glass in place? Go to a church or synagogue that has a stained glass window and look at the scenes or designs. Be sure to go inside the building so that you can see the light coming through the windows.

Stained glass windows require much time and skill. Fortunately, there is a way to capture the beauty of stained glass with ordinary materials. You can make a stained glass window from paper! First, you create a design for a stained glass window on a sheet of heavyweight paper or thin cardboard. By cutting out holes in the paper and repapering them with sheets of transparent or semitransparent colored paper, you create a stained glass effect.

Materials

Heavyweight black construction paper

Lightweight colored paper that is thin enough to let some light get through (Visit an art supply store and ask the clerk to show you a selection of papers: onionskin, rice paper, cellophane, and transparent contact paper.)

Scissors

White glue

A.
B.
C.
D.
E.
F.
TRANSLUCENT PAPER

Ways With Windows

1. To make your design, experiment with cutting out designs from a sheet of heavyweight paper. Try folding the paper as shown.

2. Draw a design along the closed fold of the triangle.

3. Carefully snip out your design and unfold the paper. The basic frame of your stained glass window will look something like F.

You might want to experiment with inexpensive paper until you get a pattern that you like.

4. After deciding on the colors you will use to cover the holes in the construction paper, trace a shape for each hole on the colors you have selected. Use the heavyweight construction paper as your tracing guide.

5. Use scissors to cut out each colored piece of paper you trace, being careful to leave at least a ¼ in. (1 cm) border for each piece.

6. Put a thin strip of white glue on the border of each piece and paste it into place on the construction paper.

7. When the glue dries you are ready to use your window. Tape it to a window in your house and enjoy the colors of your own "stained glass" window.

JAPAN

The Daruma Doll

Young boys and girls in Japan play with Daruma dolls, and these dolls are ideal gifts for children in the United States. The Daruma doll is named after a religious leader who preached a belief about life and nature called Zen Buddhism. It is said that he sat in one place for 9 years thinking and praying, became paralyzed, and had to roll himself around to tell people about his beliefs. Daruma dolls are made so that they roll back into an upright position whenever they are tipped over. You can make a Daruma doll by attaching paper cones to a base made out of half a rubber ball.

Materials (for each pair)
Hollow rubber ball
X-acto knife or razor blade
2 sticks of modeling clay
2 sheets of heavyweight colored
    construction paper
Cellophane tape
Masking tape
Watercolors or tempera paints

Daruma Doll Directions
   1. Cut the ball in half with an X-acto knife or single-edge razor blade. Be careful not to cut your fingers.
   2. Fill each half of the ball with modeling clay.
   3. Make two construction paper cones that will fit over the filled top of each ball. Tape the sides of each cone together.
   4. Using the masking tape, tape the cones to half of each ball.
   5. Paint faces on each Daruma doll.

POLAND

Paper Cutouts

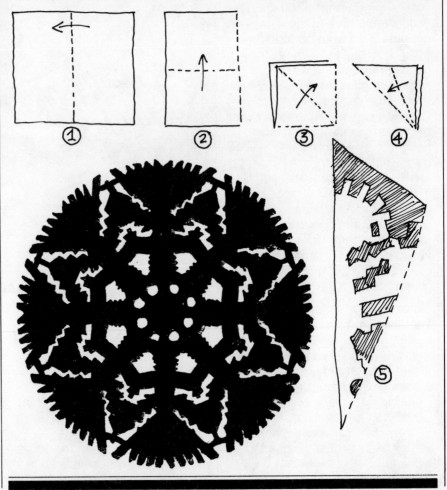

Boys and girls in Poland delight in creating beautiful paper cutouts. They fold thin paper in a special way and carefully cut out a fancy design. The paper cutouts are decorative additions to gift wrappings or windows. Here is a pattern you can try. Perhaps it will inspire you to be more "designing" yourself.

A Cutout Caper
   1. Get a 10 in. (25 cm) square of thin paper.
   2. Fold the paper along the broken lines as shown in steps 1 through 4. The dotted lines show places that have already been folded.
   3. Cut out the shaded areas as shown in step 5. Now unfold your cutout.
   Invent your own designs. Try gluing your paper cut outs onto different colored sheets of paper.

MEXICO
Piñata Project

An important part of many celebrations in Mexico is the breaking of a piñata. A piñata is a papier-mâché animal, clown, or other shape that is stuffed with small candies, money, and tiny toys and hung from a tree branch. Young children take turns trying to break the piñata with a stick. After the piñata is broken, the children scramble around to gather up the scattered goodies. Here's how to make a piñata in the shape of an animal.

Materials
Large balloon (for the body)
Small balloon (for the head)
Newspapers
Flour
Mixing bowl
2 ft. (about 60 cm) of colored yarn
Scrap sheets of colored construction
 paper
Colored tissue paper
Cardboard tubes (for the neck and
 legs)
White glue
Water

Masking tape
Candies and small change

Piñata Procedure
1. Make a paste of equal parts of flour and water in the mixing bowl.
2. Inflate both balloons and tie the ends of each in a knot.
3. Tear the newspaper into strips about 1½ in. (4 cm) wide and about 1 ft. (30 cm) long.
4. Dip each strip into the paste mixture and squeeze off the excess paste.
5. Layer both balloons with strips. Go back and forth, crisscrossing the balloons until you've built up a layer two strips thick.
6. Let the strips dry for 6 to 12 hours. Then add more layers until you have at least five layers. Let the balloons dry overnight.
7. After the strips are completely dry, push a pin through each of the layered balloons to burst them.
8. Cut a hole about 1½ in. (4 cm) across in each shape at the spot where you want the small balloon shape (head) to join the larger balloon shape (body).
9. Reach into each shape and pull out the pieces of balloon.
10. Pour candies into each shape.
11. Fasten the head to the body by fitting a short cardboard tube into the holes on the head and body shapes. This tube will be the neck. Use masking tape to fasten the shapes to the neck and to each other.
12. Add some original finishing touches to your piñata. Paste colored tissue paper over the newspaper strips. Give your animal legs of small cardboard tubes. Add a yarn tail and cut out and paste on construction-paper eyes, ears, and other features.

Now you are all set. Tie the piñata to a tree branch, ceiling, or top of a door frame. Invite some young children over and let them have fun breaking the piñata and collecting its contents.

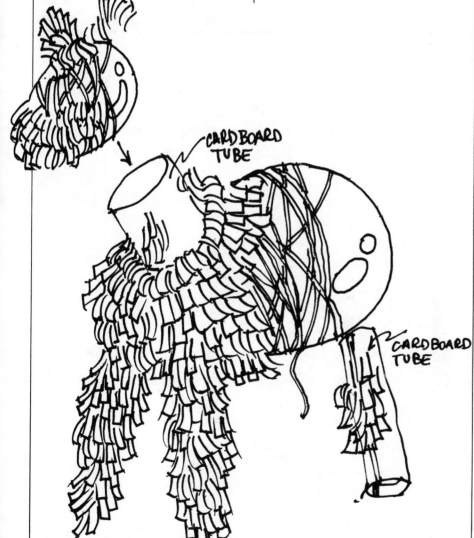

CARDBOARD TUBE

CARDBOARD TUBE

PHILIPPINES
A Model Vinta

Many people in the Philippines are skilled sailors. One of the boats they like to use, the vinta, is a dugout canoe with double outriggers to prevent tipping. You can make your own model vinta without fear of rocking the boat. It'll be clear sailing if you follow our directions!

Materials
Heavyweight paper
Tan or light brown crayon
Tape
Scissors
2 pipe cleaners
3 soda straws
Glue
Strip of thin cardboard 2 in. × ¾ in. (about 5 cm × 2 cm)
Lightweight paper
2 thin sticks or straws
Thread

Vinta Venture

1. Reproduce the pattern on a thick piece of folded paper, putting the bottom of the pattern on the fold. Cut out the pattern and use a tan or light brown crayon to make a thick covering of crayon on all its sides. This will waterproof the paper. Tape the ends (marked "xxxxxxx" on the pattern) together.

2. Punch four holes in the boat's body and put the pipe cleaners through the holes.

3. Twist the ends of the pipe cleaners around two soda straws.

4. Take the cardboard, bend the ends, and punch a hole in the middle.

5. Slit both ends of a soda straw. Bend out the sides of the soda straw on one end. Glue this end of the straw to the bottom of the boat. Slide the cardboard down the straw and glue it to the sides of the boat. The straw, or mast of the boat, should be straight when everything dries.

6. Cut a square sail from a thin sheet of paper. Color or paint it brightly.

7. Fold the top and bottom of the sail around thin sticks or straws.

8. Tie a thread from one end of the top of the sail to the other. Hang the sail by putting the thread through the slit at the top of the straw mast.

Congratulations! You have just made a vinta.

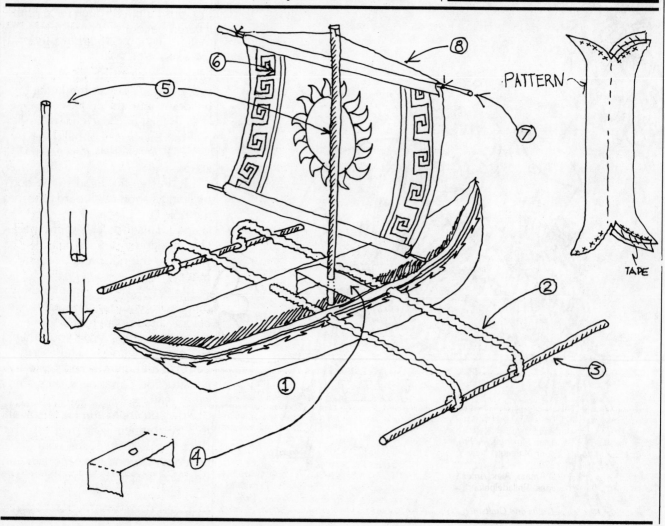

PATTERN

TAPE

THE UKRAINE (U.S.S.R.)

Pysanka Egg

In the Ukraine, an area in Southwestern Russia, people are skilled at dyeing eggshells with delicate designs. The decorated eggshells are used as Christmas tree ornaments, arranged in a basket, or simply placed on a shelf.

Pysanka egg decoration requires an empty white eggshell. To remove the yolk and white of a raw egg without breaking the shell, perform the following feat:

1. Make a small hole in the narrow end of the eggshell with a pin. Pierce the shell and wiggle the pin to make the hole larger than a pinhole. Take the pin out.

2. Now make a pinhole in the fat end of the egg. Wiggle the pin around until you've made a hole about ½ in. (less than 2 cm) across. Take the pin out.

3. Hold the egg so that the fat end (with the large hole) is over a bowl. Now blow through the hole in the small end. The white and yolk will come out the large hole.

You are now ready to proceed with your Pysanka.

Materials
White crayon
Easter egg dyes (red, yellow, blue)
Matches
Candle

Pysanka Egg Embellishment
1. Using the white crayon, draw a design on the egg.
2. Prepare bowls of red, yellow, and blue easter egg dye according to the package directions.

3. Dye the egg yellow and blot it dry.

4. Use the crayon to cover other parts of the egg.

5. Dye the egg red and blot it dry.

6. Use the crayon to cover still other parts of the egg.

7. Dye the egg blue and blot it dry.

8. Now you are ready to remove the wax that protects the yellow and red areas. Light the candle and hold the egg near the flame. As the wax on the egg melts, carefully wipe it off with a tissue.

After making one Pysanka egg to our eggs-act specifications, you may wish to experiment with different designs and colors.

Sourcebooks

Blue Mountain Crafts Council. *Joy of Crafts.* New York: Holt, Rinehart and Winston, 1975.

Creekmore, Betsey Beeler. *Making Gifts From Oddments and Outdoor Materials.* New York: Hearthside Press, 1970.

D'Amato, Janet, and D'Amato, Alex. *American Indian Craft Inspirations.* Philadelphia: Lippincott, 1972.

Gardi, Renee. *African Crafts and Craftsmen.* New York: Van Nostrand Reinhold, 1969.

Green, Henry Gordon. *A Heritage of Canadian Handicrafts.* Toronto: McClelland and Stewart, 1967.

Lavaivre, Noelle. *A Book Full of Ideas.* New York: St. Martin's Press, 1972.

Lyford, Cassie Alberta. *Iroquois Crafts.* Lawrence, Kans.: Department of the Interior, Bureau of Indian Affairs, Division of Education, 1970. Distributed by the Publication Service, Haskell Institute.

Plummer, Beverly. *Earth Presents.* New York: Atheneum Books, 1974.

Stapleton, Marjorie. *Make Things Grandma Made.* New York: Taplinger, 1975.

Wigginton, Eliot, ed. *The Foxfire Book.* Garden City, N.Y.: Doubleday, Anchor Books, 1972.

_____. *Foxfire 2.* Garden City, N.Y.: Doubleday, Anchor Books, 1975.

_____. *Foxfire 3.* Garden City, N.Y.: Doubleday, Anchor Books, 1975.

12

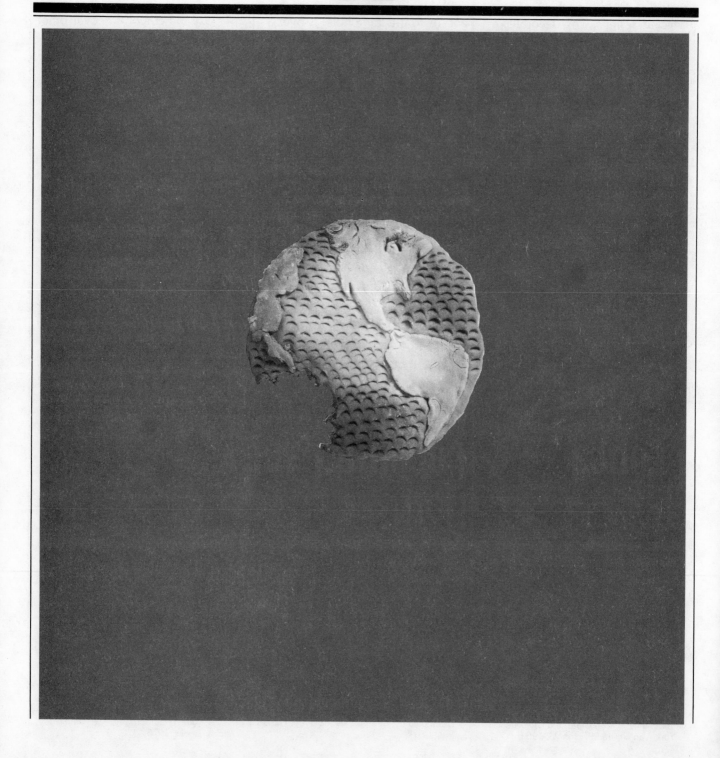

Foods (Earthpeople Munchies)

One of the things that all earthpeople share, whether they are black, brown, red, white, young, or old, is a love for munching. The foods that some people eat may seem a bit strange to you at first, but you may acquire a taste for them after all. Just think of all those lucky Chinese people crunch-munching almond cookies, Nigerians sipping peanut soup, and Canadians from the province of Quebec slurping a wintertime dessert called sugar on snow. If your stomach has never encountered almond cookies, peanut soup, or sugar on snow, it (and you) has really been missing out.

In this chapter you'll be able to sample some international munchies. We have collected recipes that come from earthpeople both far and near, recipes that are easy to make and require readily available ingredients and utensils. As you eat what people from different countries eat, you'll be getting some food for thought.

BELGIUM

Speculoos

Boys and girls in Belgium receive their Christmas gifts on December 6. The night before, they put their shoes by the fireplace along with a carrot and a piece of bread. Although Santa Claus is not part of their Christmas, Saint Nicolat will fill their shoes with small gifts. The carrot is for Saint Nicolat's donkey and the bread is for Saint Nicolat. Does the name "Saint Nicolat" sound like another name used for Santa Claus?

To celebrate the Christmas season, people in Belgium make these cookies.

½ c. softened butter
1 c. brown sugar
2 c. sifted flour
½ tsp. cinnamon
½ tsp. baking powder
pinch of salt
pinch of nutmeg
Yield: 2 to 3 doz.

For a Sackful of Speculoos
1. Mix the butter and sugar together thoroughly, using a fork to press the sugar through the butter. Then add the flour, ⅛ c. at a time, blending well each time. Sprinkle the mixture with some water to keep it moist. Form the dough into a ball, cover it, and place it in the refrigerator to chill overnight.
2. The next day, add the other ingredients and reshape the dough into a ball. Chill for 2 or 3 hours.
3. Roll out the dough about ½ in. (1 cm) thick on a floured board. Use cookie cutters with holiday shapes on the cookies.
4. Place your cookies on greased cookie sheets and bake them in a 350° oven for 12-15 minutes. Check on them after 10 minutes.
5. Share your tasty speculoos. There is plenty for all.

BRAZIL

Fancy Hot Chocolate

2 sq. unsweetened chocolate
1 qt. milk
2 egg yolks
2 tbsp. granulated sugar
Yield: 4 to 6 cups

The Chocolate Chef
1. Melt the chocolate in a 2 qt. saucepan.
2. Slowly add the warm milk to the melted chocolate.
3. When the chocolate has dissolved in the milk, remove the saucepan from the heat.
4. In a mixing bowl, beat the egg yolks and sugar together.
5. Add the egg yolk/sugar mixture to the chocolate milk.
6. Reheat this until a "skin" forms at the top. Do not boil.
7. You now have fancy hot chocolate that you can serve with or without whipped cream.

fancy hot chocolate

BRAZIL

Biscoitos de Maizena

Biscoitos de Maizena

Does the word "biscoitos" appear familiar to you? It's like the English word "biscuits." "De" means "of." What do you think "maizena" means? Look up the word "maize" in a dictionary.

2 c. cornstarch
1 c. granulated sugar
$\frac{1}{2}$ tsp. salt
1 egg, slightly beaten
$\frac{3}{4}$ c. butter, softened
Vanilla extract
Yield: 30 cookies

Biscoito Business
1. Mix all the ingredients thoroughly, except the butter and vanilla.
2. Add the butter to the mixture and knead it.
3. Add 2 or 3 drops of vanilla and knead the dough some more.
4. Preheat oven to 375°.
5. Shape the dough into little balls 12 to 15 in. (about 30 to 40 cm) in diameter and place them on well-greased cookie sheets.
6. Bake cookies for about 7 minutes.

CANADA

Sugar on Snow

This is a very popular treat in Canada and in the Northeastern United States, where there is a large supply of maple sugar and snow. To make this treat, people collect the sap from sugar maple trees and gather clean snow. Even if you don't live in a place that has sugar maple trees and snow, all is not lost. Follow our recipe.

2 trays ice cubes or 2 c. snow
1 c. maple-flavored pancake syrup or maple syrup
Yield: 8 servings

Sugar on "Snow Job"

1. Put 8 empty cups in the freezer about an hour before you start "cooking."

2. Then, if you have snow, fill each cup with ¼ c. snow. Or, wrap 2 or 3 ice cubes in a towel and pound on them with a hammer or rolling pin. Repeat for all the ice cubes. Fill each cup in the freezer with crushed ice.

3. Pour the syrup into a saucepan and heat it for about 5 minutes.

4. Take the cups of snow or ice out of the freezer.

5. Remove the syrup from the heat and pour 1 or 2 tbsp. hot syrup over each cup of snow.

6. Pass out 8 teaspoons. No further directions needed beyond this point!

Sugar on Snow

CHINA

Almond Cookies

almond cookie

$1\frac{1}{2}$ c. flour
1 tsp. salt
$\frac{1}{2}$ tsp. soda
6 tbsp. shortening
$\frac{1}{2}$ tsp. almond extract
1 egg
$\frac{1}{4}$ c. granulated sugar
10 blanched almonds
1 egg yolk, beaten with 1 tbsp. water
Yield: 10 cookies

Going Nuts Over Cookies

1. Blanch the almonds by covering them with cold water and bringing it to a boil for a minute or two. The skins will slip off easily after you drain off the water.

2. Knead all the ingredients together, except the almonds and egg yolk mixture, until you have a soft dough.

3. Preheat the oven to 350°.

4. Make 10 flat cookies from the dough and place them on a greased cookie sheet.

5. Brush the top of each cookie with the egg yolk/water mixture.

6. Place an almond in the center of each cookie.

7. Bake the cookies for 10 minutes, or until they are golden brown.

CHINA

Egg Drop Soup

A Chinese soup that is tasty, nutritious, and very easy to make is egg drop soup, so called because one of its ingredients is a well-beaten egg that is dropped. Dropped where? Now that we've dropped this hint, try the recipe and find out.

4 c. water
2 chicken bouillon cubes
$\frac{1}{2}$ tsp. salt
$\frac{1}{2}$ tsp. pepper
2 tbsp. cornstarch
4 tbsp. cold water
1 egg
1 tbsp. chopped parsley
Yield: 4 servings

Directions to Egg You On

1. Bring the 4 c. water to a slow boil in a saucepan.

2. Dissolve the bouillon cubes in the water.

3. Add the salt and pepper to the water.

4. Make a thickener for the soup by putting 2 tbsp. cornstarch into a small cup and mixing in 4 tbsp. cold water. Make sure that the cornstarch is thoroughly dissolved.

5. Add the cornstarch thickener to the boiling soup.

6. Break the egg into a cup, beat it with a fork, and add it to the soup.

7. Pour the soup into 4 bowls and sprinkle each serving with a little chopped parsley.

8. Sit up straight as you eat your soup. (A soup-ine position is not advised.)

FINLAND

Banana Voileipä

Banana Voileipa

Does the thought of a banana sandwich ap-peel to you? Banana voileipä, a tasty and nutritious dessert from Finland, is really a banana sandwich in fancy dress.

10 graham crackers
Soft butter or margarine
Currant or blueberry jam
Ripe banana
Yield: 5 sandwiches

The Well-Dressed Banana

1. Spread each graham cracker with butter or margarine. Each of these crackers will be a sandwich half.

2. Add a dab of jam to the crackers.

3. Slice the bananas and put a few slices on 5 of your graham crackers.

4. Use the remaining crackers as the sandwich tops.

FRANCE

Crêpes

Crêpes are very thin French pancakes. The French enjoy crêpes both as an entrée and a dessert. We're going to cater to your sweet tooth here.

1 c. sifted flour
Pinch of salt
1 tbsp. powdered sugar
6 eggs, slightly beaten
1 tbsp. melted butter
1 tbsp. orange flavoring
1 c. water
Yield: 2 doz.

Flipping Over Crêpes

1. Sift the flour, salt, and sugar into a large mixing bowl.
2. Slowly stir the eggs and melted butter into the flour.
3. Beat this mixture until it is completely smooth. You may wish to use a blender at this point.
4. Add the orange flavoring to the water and add it to the batter a little at a time. Stir as you add the water.
5. Cover the bowl with foil or a clean cloth and let it stand in the refrigerator several hours or overnight.
6. Grease a griddle or frying pan with a bit of butter or margarine and heat it.
7. When the griddle is hot pour about 2 tbsp. batter onto it. After about a minute, use a pancake flipper to turn the crêpes. Add a little butter or margarine to the griddle each time or the crêpes will stick.
8. Stack the crêpes on a plate as you go along. To prepare, sprinkle some powdered sugar, honey, or syrup on each crêpe, roll it up, and enjoy!

HAITI

Coconut Candy

Boys and girls in Haiti enjoy this coconut candy.

3 c. brown sugar, packed
1 c. milk
Pinch of salt
1 tsp. vanilla
½ tsp. nutmeg
2 tbsp. butter
1 c. shredded coconut
Yield: 1 doz.

Sweet Talking

1. Put the sugar, milk, and salt into a saucepan. Mix them together and cook over low heat for about 15 minutes, stirring.
2. Your candy base is ready when a *small* spoonful becomes firm when dropped into a cup of cold water. Try to make it into a soft ball with your fingers while it's in the water. If you can't, keep heating the mixture until you get a small sample to the soft ball stage.
3. Take the pan off the stove. Add the other ingredients and beat the mixture with a wooden spoon until thick.
4. Pour it onto a flat greased dish.
5. Before the candy has cooled completely, cut it into squares.

IRAN
Mâst Va Khiar

Yogurt is a very important part of the diet for people living in North Africa, Turkey, the Balkan countries, and Iran. A healthful food, it can be eaten plain or served with fresh fruits or vegetables. Yogurt with cucumbers, or mâst va khiar, is usually served as a salad or appetizer in Iran. As a snack, however, it surely takes the cake.

2 small cucumbers
2 c. plain yogurt
1 tsp. dried dill
Salt
Pepper

Mâst Method

1. Peel and seed the cucumbers and chop them into small pieces, less than ½ in. (about 1.5 cm) across.

2. Put the cucumber pieces into a mixing bowl and add the yogurt, dill, and a sprinkling of salt and pepper. Mix the ingredients well.

3. Place the mixture in the refrigerator for 2 hours.

4. Serve mâst va khiar as a creamy and cooling treat for a hot day.

ISRAEL
Apples in Honey

apples in honey

The celebration of the Jewish New Year, Rosh Hashana, is a happy time as Jews around the world look forward to a "sweet" year. Foods cooked with honey are part of the Rosh Hashana festivities, and apples in honey are a core item on many menus.

2 apples
¼ c. honey
¼ c. sugar
¼ c. water
½ tsp. cinnamon
Yield: 2 servings

Assembling Ambrosial Apples

1. Peel and core the apples.

2. Add the honey, sugar, water, and cinnamon to a saucepan. Mix well and bring the syrupy mixture to a boil.

3. Place the apples in the mixture and simmer until the apples are soft. Spoon the syrup over the apples as the mixture simmers.

4. When the apples are soft, place each on a plate and top with the remaining syrup. Eat the apples with a fork.

ITALY
Antipasto Platter

An antipasto platter is a traditional item on any Italian restaurant's menu. The antipasto is an array of sliced cheeses, meats, and vegetables that is served before the pasta (spaghetti or macaroni). Can you figure out where the name "antipasto" comes from?

$\frac{1}{4}$ lb. sliced boiled ham
$\frac{1}{4}$ lb. sliced Genoa salami
$\frac{1}{4}$ lb. sliced pepperoni
$\frac{1}{4}$ lb. sliced provolone cheese
Small can of pitted black olives
2 tomatoes
1 green pepper
5 celery stalks
Honeydew or cantaloupe, if in season
Yield: 6 servings

Platter Put-Ons

1. Arrange the sliced meats and cheeses on a large dish.

2. Drain the olives and put them in the saucer. then put the saucer on the dish.

3. Wash the tomatoes, pepper, and celery. Cut the tomatoes into ½ in. wedges. Cut the pepper in half, cut out the part with the seeds, and slice the pepper into thin sections. Cut the celery into 2 in. slices. Arrange them on your platter.

4. If you have a melon, cut it into wedges and put them on the platter.

5. Buono appetito!

antipasto platter

JAPAN

Mikan No Awayuki-Tan

"Mikan" is a small orange that we know as a mandarin orange. You can buy canned mandarin orange sections in the grocery store to make this Japanese snow sponge.

1 tbsp. of unflavored gelatin
½ c. cold water
1 small can of mandarin orange sections
2 c. granulated sugar
2 egg whites
1 tsp. vanilla extract
Yield: 16 squares

Making Light of Sponge: It's Easy!

1. Add the gelatin to the water. Pour the liquid from the oranges into a 2 c. container. Add enough water to the mandarin orange liquid to make 1½ c. liquid.
2. Put the liquid, gelatin/water mixture, and sugar into a saucepan. Bring the mixture to a boil and let it boil for 5 minutes. Remove it from the heat and let it cool.
3. Put the egg whites into a mixing bowl and beat them with an egg beater until stiff peaks form when you lift the beater.
4. Pour the cooled syrup mixture over the egg whites. Stir in the vanilla and beat the mixture.
5. Pour into an 8 in. (about 20 cm) square cake dish and place the orange sections on top. After it hardens, cut it into squares.

MEXICO

Guacamole Dip

guacamole dip

Do you know what an avocado is? If not, proceed directly to a supermarket and find one for this dip! Hint: You will find avocados lurking in the fresh food and vegetable section. Pick out two ripe avocados. They should feel soft when you gently press them. Or, buy two unripe avocados and bring them home or to school to ripen on a shelf or table for 3 or 4 days.

2 ripe avocados
1 tomato
½ lemon
Salt
Pepper
Corn or tortilla chips
Yield: 4 to 6 servings

For Guacamole Gourmets

1. Cut the avocados in half and remove the large pits.
2. Scoop the flesh out and mash in a mixing bowl, using a fork.
3. Cut the tomato in half and put the halves into a small bowl. Mash the tomatoes with a fork.
4. Blend the tomatoes into the mashed avocado.
5. Squeeze the juice from half a lemon into the avocado/tomato mixture.
6. Add salt and pepper to taste.
7. Mound the dip in a serving bowl and surround with dippers: corn or tortilla chips.

SYRIA
Pita Bread

In many countries of the Near East people eat bread of a flat, circular shape, known as pita bread in Syria. Large supermarkets in this country sometimes sell it because its large pocket is handy for sandwiches. If you've ever tried to make ordinary bread you know that you "knead" hours to make it. Pita bread is different—it's quick and easy to make.

1 pkg. dry yeast
1¼ c. warm water (110° F.)
2 tsp. honey
1 tsp. salt
3 c. flour
Yield: 6 discs

Problem-Free Pita
1. Mix the warm water and honey in a large bowl.
2. Add the yeast and put the bowl in a warm place for 5 or 10 minutes until the mixture starts to bubble.
3. Gradually stir in the salt and flour.
4. Knead the dough thoroughly.
5. Form the dough into balls and roll it out thin and flat. Make the dough circles about ¼ in. (less than 1 cm) thick and 6 to 8 in. (about 20 to 25 cm) in diameter.
6. Place the circles on a greased cookie sheet and cover them with a towel.
7. Let the dough circles rise for about 45 minutes.
8. Preheat the oven to 500° F.
9. Bake the bread for 12 to 14 minutes, or until lightly browned. The bread will soften upon cooling and will have a pocket.

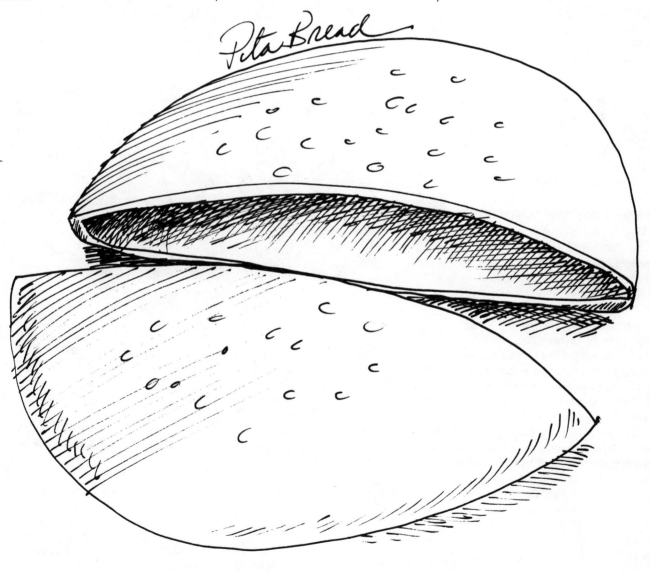

NIGERIA

Peanut Soup

We all (at least we authors!) love peanut brittle, peanut butter, or peanuts in candy, but how many of us have tasted peanut soup? The peanut is widely used in African cooking because it grows abundantly there. Try our recipe for peanut soup. It's guaranteed to make you come out of your shell.

1 sm. stick of celery
1 sm. carrot
1 sm. onion
1 lg. potato
1 lg. tomato
2 c. water
1 chicken or beef bouillon cube
1 tsp. salt
$\frac{1}{2}$ tsp. pepper
$\frac{1}{2}$ c. chunky peanut butter
$\frac{1}{2}$ c. milk
1 tbsp. brown sugar
3 tbsp. rice
Yield: 6 servings

Preparing Soup for Peanuts
1. Wash the celery, carrot, onion, potato, and tomato in water.
2. Peel the onion and potato.
3. Cut all the vegetables into very small pieces and place them in a saucepan.
4. Add the water, bouillon cube, salt, and pepper to the pan, cover, and boil very gently for 20 minutes. Stir occasionally.
5. In a mixing bowl, thoroughly blend the peanut butter, milk, and brown sugar.
6. Add this to the ingredients in the saucepan.
7. Stir in the rice.
8. Let all the ingredients simmer at low heat for 30 minutes.
9. Serve your peanut soup in soup bowls. Garnish it with chopped peanuts if you have a mad passion for peanuts.

TURKEY

Turkish Tea Cookies

Turkish Tea Cookies

These cookies are usually served with fruit juice or tea in Turkey. The question is, Do the Turks like to dunk them? We think not—these are very buttery cookies.

$\frac{1}{2}$ lb. (227 g) sweet butter
1 c. granulated sugar
2 c. sifted flour
$\frac{1}{4}$ c. blanched almonds
Yield: 60 cookies

Just in Time for Tea
1. Let the butter soften. Put the butter into a bowl and add the sugar a little at a time. Use a fork to mix the butter and sugar together until the butter and sugar are combined.
2. Add the flour a little at a time and blend it into the butter and sugar.
3. Roll out the dough about $\frac{1}{2}$ in. (less than 2 cm) thick on a board.
4. Preheat the oven to 350° F.
5. Use small, 1 in. cookie cutters to form the cookies.
6. Put the cookies on a greased cookie sheet, leaving about 2 in. between cookies. Place an almond on each cookie.
7. Bake for 10 to 15 minutes.

International Cheese Nibbling Festival

A nibbler's delight and an easy "whey" to sample foods from many lands, an international cheese festival is fun, no matter how you slice it. You will need a collection of cheeses, cheese slicers, small plates for each cheese, and perhaps an assortment of breads. You might make small "place cards" with the name of each cheese and its country.

Here is a list of countries and some cheeses for which they are famous. You can shop for these cheeses at any delicatessen or special food store.

1. **Denmark**—Havarti, Samsoë
2. **England**—Cheshire, Stilton
3. **France**—Brie, Camembert, Port du Salut, Roquefort
4. **Germany**—Limburger, Muenster
5. **Greece**—Feta, Kasseri
6. **Italy**—Bel paese, Fontina, Gorgonzola, Provolone
7. **Netherlands**—Edam, Gouda, Leyden
8. **United States**—Longhorn cheddar, Monterey jack

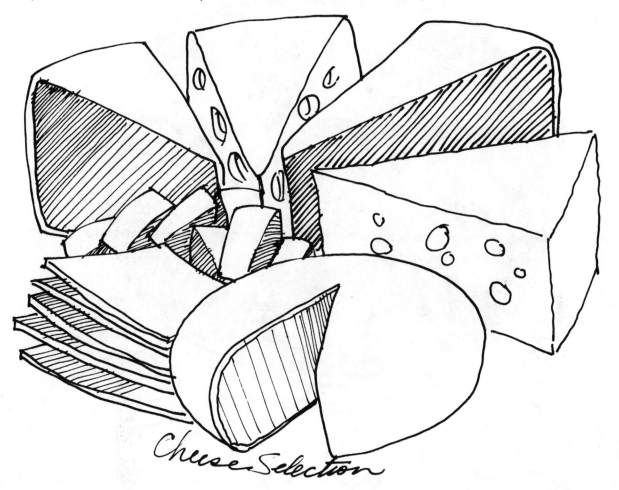

Cheese Selection

Saucebooks—Excuse Us—Sourcebooks

Angier, Bradford. *Wilderness Cookery.* Harrisburg, Pa.: Stackpole Books, 1963.

Benoît, Mme. Jehanne. *The Canadiana Cookbook.* Toronto: Burns & MacEarchern Ltd., 1970.

Darby, William J.; Ghalioungui, Paul; and Brivetti, Louis. *Food: The Gift of Osiris.* New York and London: Academic Press, 1977.

Hayes, Elizabeth S. *Spices and Herbs Around the World.* Garden City, N.Y.: Doubleday, 1961.

Herman, Judith, and Herman, Margaret Shalett. *The Cornucopia.* New York: Harper & Row, 1973.

Hughes, Stella. *Chuckwagon Cookin'.* Tucson, Ariz.: University of Arizona Press, 1974.

Nelson, Kay Shaw. *The Eastern European Cookbook.* Chicago: Henry Regnery Company, 1973.

Szathmary, Louis. *American Gastronomy.* Chicago: Henry Regnery Company, 1974.

Wason, Betty. *A Salute to Cheeses.* New York: Hawthorn Books, 1966.

Wilson, C. Anne. *Food and Drink in Britain.* London: Constable and Company Ltd., 1973.

13

Sports and Games

Earthpeople find excitement in being part of a crowd of cheering people at a baseball, basketball, football, or soccer game. Earthpeople also enjoy participating in sports and games. Every country and every culture on this earth has sporting events.

The games we play or watch reflect our culture. This chapter will give you many insights into people as you learn about and even play the sports and games of different countries.

Earthpeople enjoy sports. We play sports, watch sporting events, argue about sports, and make stars of our favorite athletes. Magazines, books, films, and songs about athletes are common in every country. Cities sponsor parades when a local athlete sets a new world record or when a local team has won a championship.

Countries sometimes honor an athlete or sporting event by issuing postage stamps. Postage stamps that feature athletes or athletics are a source of social and physical information about the countries of the earth.

On the following pages we show you some stamp starter cards to start you collecting and studying sports stamps. Each card displays a few stamps that you can search for. There are, of course, hundreds of other stamps. Try out the following activities on each stamp that you acquire.

1. Find out its country of issue. The countries use their own names for themselves on the stamps, so you will need to call your resources as a detective into play.

2. Printed on each country's stamp is its face value—the amount of money that the stamp costs. Find out what unit of currency is used in the country. The name for the money, for example, the Italian lire (lira), or a symbol for it will be on the stamp.

3. Figure out how much the stamp would cost in your own country's money. The financial section of newspapers with a large circulation sometimes lists the values of the various currencies, and any local bank has daily information on money values.

4. Try some sports-related climate geography with your sports stamps. Find out whether the sports that a country takes pride in are well suited to that country's climate.

5. Do some map work. Locate each country for which you collect a sports stamp.

References

These three lists give you some names and addresses for more information about stamps and stamp collecting.

Stamp Magazines

Australian Stamp News
Sterling Street
Dubbo, N.S.W., Australia
Linn's Stamp News
Box 29
Sidney, OH 45365
Mekeel's Weekly Stamp News
Box 1660
Portland, ME 04104
Minkus Stamp Journal
116 West 32nd Street
New York, NY 10001
Scott Monthly Journal
10102 F Street
Omaha, NE 68127

Stamp Collecting
42 Maiden Lane
London, WCZE711, England
Stamps
153 Waverly Place
New York, NY 10014
Western Stamp Collector
Box 10
Albany, OR 97321

Stamp Clubs

American First Day Cover Society
626 Woodward Building
Washington, D.C. 20005
American Philatelic Society
Box 800
State College, PA 16801
American Stamp Dealers' Association
147 West 42nd Street
New York, NY 10036
American Topical Association
3308 North 50th
Milwaukee, WI 53216
Bureau Issues Association
19 Maple Street
Arlington, MA 02174
Society of Philatelic Americans
P.O. Box 42060
Cincinnati, OH 45242

Stamp Reference Books

Bloomgarden, Henry S. *American History Through Geometric Stamps.* New York: Arco Publishing, 1969.
Boggs, Winthrop. *The Postage Stamps and Postal History of Canada.* Lawrence, Mass.: Quarterman Publications, 1974.
Lidman, David. *Treasury of Stamps.* New York: Abrams, 1975.
Martin, M. W. *Topical Stamp Collecting.* New York: Arco Publishing, 1975.
Scott Standard Postage Stamp Catalogue. New York: Scott Publishing, 1978.
Storer, Doug. *Amazing but True Stories Behind the Stamps.* New York: Pocket Books, 1976.
Thorp, Prescott H. *The Complete Guide to Stamp Collecting.* New York, 1953.
United States Stamps and Stories. New York: Scott Publishing, 1973. Published for the United States Postal Service.

SPORTS STAMPS

Starter Cards
Each of these starter cards has pictures of a few stamps honoring a particular sport. Try to collect these stamps and many others picturing athletes or sporting events.

EQUESTRIAN

HOCKEY

SKIING

RUNNING

WATER SPORTS

SOCCER

OTHER

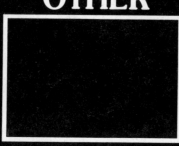

North American Indian Toys and Games

After reading these brief descriptions of games that the young people of various North American Indian tribes played, you may be inspired to try some of them with your friends. The question is, are you game? For each game, think about the following:

1. Is it a toy or game for younger or older children?

2. What kinds of materials, if any, does the toy or game require?

3. In what part of North America did the young players live?

4. Does the toy or game teach any skill that might be useful to young people when the become adults?

5. Are there any modern versions of the toy or game?

Spinning Tops

Youngsters in many Indian tribes played spinning-top games. In the Hopi tribe the men of the village carved tops made of wood and spun by a rawhide whip. To get the top to spin, children first wrapped the rawhide around a notch cut in the center of the top. The whip was then quickly cracked, which sent the top whirling. Carefully striking the whip on the notch kept the top spinning.

The Eskimo Buzz

This noisemaker toy was used by Eskimo children. Indian children in the Southwestern United States had similar noisemakers.

Eskimos made the toy by drilling two holes in a small piece of bone and threading a cord through them. (Americans Indians of the Southwest used wood or leather in place of bone.) The cord was tied so that the child could hold one of the ends of the loop of cord in each hand. The child pulled on the cord and then loosened it. The bone spun, making a whirring or buzzing sound.

Ball Games

Racketball

This was a team game in which each team tried to get a ball that was 4 in. (about 6 cm) in diameter through a set of goal posts. Each team member had a racket with a small rawhide net at one end. Players could carry the ball in their rackets or throw it to another player's racket but could not touch it. The players also used their rackets to slow down or stop opposing players. Many different tribes enjoyed this rough-and-tumble game, including the Creek, Iroquois, Penobscot, Shoshoni, and Chippewa.

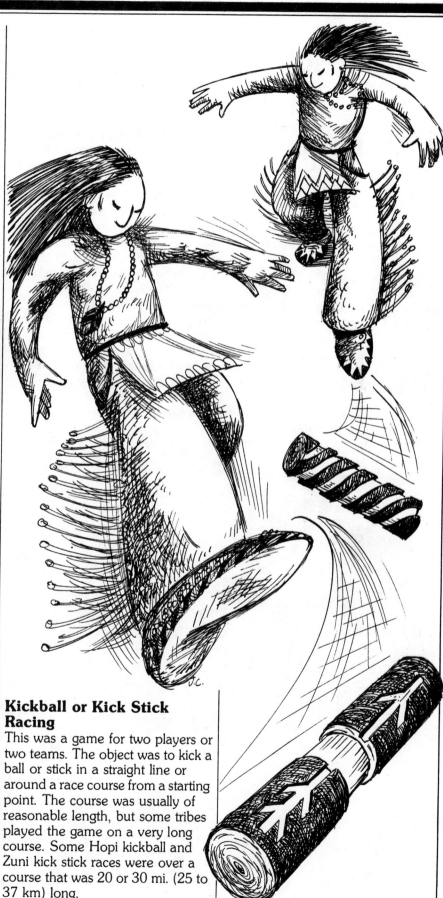

Kickball or Kick Stick Racing

This was a game for two players or two teams. The object was to kick a ball or stick in a straight line or around a race course from a starting point. The course was usually of reasonable length, but some tribes played the game on a very long course. Some Hopi kickball and Zuni kick stick races were over a course that was 20 or 30 mi. (25 to 37 km) long.

Some Games From Different Countries

AFGHANISTAN
Mirbadakan,
A BALL GAME

This game calls for two teams of four to twelve players each, a large rubber ball about the size of a soccer ball, and a bat. To prepare the playing field, draw two lines about 150 ft. (45 m) apart. The lines should be about 50 ft. (15 m) long. If you are playing on grass you can simply mark the ends of the lines. One of these lines is the goal line, the other is the batting line.

The first team at bat lines up near the batting line. One member of the other team is the pitcher. The others are fielders and spread themselves around the space along the goal line.

The pitcher stands about 25 ft. (7.6 m) from the batter. Each batter gets three tries to hit the ball, which is pitched underhand. If the batter hits the ball, he or she must drop the bat, run to the goal line, and run back to the batting line. The fielders try to tag the running batter with the ball. The batter who gets back to the batting line without being hit scores a run. Each batter gets a turn until one batter is tagged. The teams then switch sides. The team that scores the most runs in five innings wins.

CHILE
A Marble Game

This marble game is for two or more players. Each player needs ten marbles. One of the players cuts holes in a shoe box, numbering the smallest hole with the highest number and the largest hole with the lowest number, so that it looks like the one in the illustration.

After deciding on the order of play, begin. Each player gets five tries to shoot a marble into one of the holes in the box. The marble shooter must be at a distance of about 6½ ft. (2 m). If a player's marble goes into a hole, the player who has prepared the shoe box pays the shooter the number of marbles shown above the hole. If the shooter misses, the shoe box boss gets to keep the shooter's marble.

LUXEMBOURG

Zabott

Zabott is a good game for six or more players, requiring nothing else but an old shoe. One player is chosen to be It. The other players sit together in a circle and It stands in the middle.

One of the players in the circle holds the old shoe behind his or her back. The players pass the shoe around behind their backs and try to confuse It about the location of the shoe. As they pass the shoe around the circle, the players sing:

Shoe, shoe
It stands, it walks
It gobbles, it wobbles
It got away from me.
It tries to tag the person holding the shoe. If It tags the correct player, the player becomes It. If It is wrong, he or she must remain in the circle.

On the Ball: Sourcebooks for Sports and Games

Anderson, Bob, ed. *Sportsource.* Mountain View, Calif. World Publications, 1975.

Arlott, John, ed. *The Oxford Companion to World Sports and Games.* London, New York: Oxford University Press, 1975.

Bell, Robert C., ed. *Board and Table Games From Many Civilizations.* Fairlawn, N.J.: Oxford University Press, 1968.

Brasch, Rudolph. *How Did Sports Begin? A Look at the Origins of Man At Play.* New York: David McKay, 1970.

Cozens, Frederick W., and Stumpf, Florence Scovil. *Sports in American Life.* New York: Arno Press, 1976.

Fluegelman, Andrew, ed. *The New Games Book.* Garden City, N.Y.: Doubleday, 1976.

Harris, Harold Arthur. *Sports In Greece and Rome.* Ithaca, N.Y.: Cornell University Press, 1972.

Jones, Wally, and Washington, Joe. *Black Champions Challenge American Sports.* New York: David McKay, 1972.

Klafs, Carl E., and Lyon, M. Joan. *The Female Athlete: Conditioning, Competition, and Culture.* St. Louis: Mosby, 1973.

McConville, Robert. *History of Board Games.* Palo Alto, Calif.: Creative Publications, 1974.

Menke, Frank Grant. *The Encyclopedia of Sports.* South Brunswick, N.J.: A. S. Barnes, 1975.

Nueckle, Susan. *Selected Guide to Sports and Recreation Books.* New York: Fleet Press, 1974.

Rooney, John F., Jr. *A Geography of American Sports: From Cabin Creek to Anaheim.* Reading, Mass.: Addison Wesley Publishing Co., 1974.

Tutho, Thomas A., and Bruns, William. *Winning Is Everything and Other American Myths.* New York: Macmillan, 1976.

Webster's Sports Dictionary. Springfield, Mass.: G. & C. Merriam, 1976.

Wise, Sydney F., and Fisher, Douglas. *Canada's Sporting Heroes.* Ontario: General Publishing, 1974.

Withers, Carl. *Treasury of Games.* New York: Grosset & Dunlap, 1976.

14

Part IV/Peopledoings Around the World

Music

Imagine for a moment that, hovering in space, you are listening to the sounds our planet pours forth. Listen very carefully. . . . Can you hear the sounds of people shouting and crying? Can you also hear people talking and laughing? If you listen very, very carefully you'll hear something else—the sound of music.

At this very moment, somewhere in Uganda a mother is singing a lullabye to a crying child. Somewhere in Australia a truckdriver is singing a country western song in a truck that roars down a lonesome highway. Somewhere out West in the United States a cowboy with an $8 guitar is strumming a song about beautiful sunsets. Somewhere in England a rock-and-roll band is striking a chord in the hearts of its audience.

The music of the earth captures our sadness and our joy. Yesterday, today, and tomorrow are all present in the music and words of our songs. This chapter will help you understand that the music of our planet is both an individual and universal expression of the people who create it.

FOLK SONGS FROM FOLKS AROUND THE WORLD*

Tune into some songs that are favorites of young people in five countries. The words of each song appear in the language of the country and in English. The melody is easy to pick out on a guitar or piano. Gather a group of friends together and face the music. You'll learn about earthpeople from various countries—a noteworthy accomplishment.

*These five songs are all from Carl S. Miller, ed., *Sing, Children, Sing* (New York: Chappell, 1972). Distributed by Quadrangle Books. Copyright © 1972 by the U.S. Committee for UNICEF. The words and music to these songs are used with the permission of the U.S. Committee for UNICEF.

BRAZIL

Ciranda

The song on page 132 is a Brazilian singing game. The players stand in a circle, hold hands, and sing the song together once through. Then the players in turn go into the center of the circle to sing a verse by themselves. After each verse the other players sing the chorus.

Be a Busybody About Brazil

1. What is the original language of the song?** Locate Brazil on a world map. Locate the country that its language comes from. Do some research to find out why the people in Brazil speak the same language as a country so distant.

2. On a world map compare the size of Brazil to the size of the state, province, or county in which you live. Would you say that Brazil is one of the larger or smaller countries of the world?

3. What is the capital of Brazil? What is its largest city? Have you ever heard of either of these two cities? Find each city on a map of Brazil. Can you explain why the capital of the country is so far inland? If you can't, you're guilty of a "capital" offense. (Do some research!)

**Portuguese.

English version of the words:

1. Ciranda, cirandinha,
   L-t's all do the ciranda;
   Let us give a half turn,
   And again a turn and a half.

2. The ring that you gave me
   Was made of glass and broke;
   The love you felt for me
   Was so little that it's gone.

3. And so, Miss (name)...
   Step into this circle;
   Say a very pretty verse,
   Say goodbye and you may leave.

GHANA

Kye Kye Kole

Ca-ca-shi-lan-ga, ca-ca-shi-lan-ga. Koom-ma-dye-day, Koom-ma-dye-day.

This is a singing game from the country of Ghana. The players form a circle and pick a leader to be at its center. The leader begins singing the song, hands on head. The players then follow the leader's singing and movements as the song continues. The leader sings the next phrase in the song, hands on shoulders, and the next, hands on hips. On the last phrase, the leader falls down and the group does the same. Then the leader gets up and tries to tag one of the players, who tries to run away. The players cannot get up until the leader does. The person tagged by the leader is the next leader.

Most of the words to this song are nonsense words with no real meanings.

Ghana: Go to It!
1. Locate the country of Ghana on a world map. What are its neighboring countries?
2. Use a reference book to find out about Ghana. When did Ghana become an independent country? What languages are spoken there? What type of climate does Ghana enjoy? What kinds of crops grow there?

LEBANON
Ya Ghizayyel

Can you guess what the word "ghizayyel" means in English? Hint: It's the name of a small desert antelope. Look at the word again. . . . Did you guess "gazelle"?

This song is about the gazelle, an animal that runs gracefully and is able to leap tall boulders at a single bound. Have you ever seen motion pictures of gazelles running and leaping as they race across the landscape?

Let's Look into Lebanon
1. Find the country of Lebanon on a map. What countries surround it?
2. Do some research on the languages spoken in Lebanon and the major religions of its people.
3. Find out about current events in Lebanon that have affected both the country and its neighbors. What do you think the future holds for this country? Will Lebanon have peace or war in the years to come? Are there countries or groups of people in the world who might cause problems for Lebanon or who are interested in helping Lebanon have a peaceful future?

Gaily

Ya ghi-zay-yel ya bul - hi - ba
Ya hel - wa ya m'aaz - i - bah, Ya (a) mee - ni
khab - ber ha - li. La - fa __ 'a - sheer es - see - ba.

JAMAICA

Little Sally Water

Let's play another singing game, this one from Jamaica. To sing and play it, boys and girls join hands and form a circle with one person at its center. The person in the center imitates Sally Water as the words of the song direct. Sally—Sammy, for you boys—crouches down in the center of the circle at first and begins to rise as the song progresses. Toward the end of the song Sally or Sammy picks a partner and brings her or him into the center of the circle. Then the song begins again with the new Sally or Sammy at its center.

An Armchair Journey to Jamaica

1. Find the country of Jamaica on a world map. What countries are a "Ship's throw" away? Compare the size of Jamaica with that of your state, province, or county.

2. Do some research to find out where the original Jamaicans came from and how and why they went to Jamaica.

3. What kind of climate do you think that Jamaica has? Research your response. What crops does this climate nurture?

4. Visit a travel agency to get pamphlets about a Jamaican vacation. What cities seem to be the most popular tourist areas?

5. Interview some people who have recently visited Jamaica to get their opinion about what life is like in Jamaica. What did they think about the residents of Jamaica they met? How did they like Jamaican food and music? Would they return to Jamaica for another visit? In your opinion, did they interact with the Jamaicans and Jamaica?

Guitar:
X = hand clap

Brightly

Lit - tle Sal - ly Wa - ter sprink-le in the sau - cer.

(claps cont.)

Rise, Sal - ly, rise an' wipe your weep-ing eyes; Sal - ly, turn to the

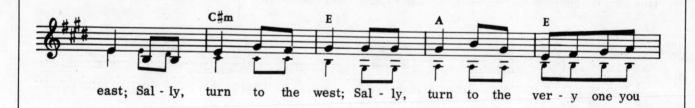

east; Sal - ly, turn to the west; Sal - ly, turn to the ver - y one you

love the best. Then you hov-er up and you pick her up, And you

put her in a gold - en room, my dar - ling; Hov - er up and you

pick her up, And you put her in a gold - en room,

TANZANIA

Leemweh

Tanzanian children sing this song to learn how to count. Its words are the numbers from one to ten in the Rimi or Tutu language. The person singing the song starts with the left hand outstretched and turns each finger over with the right hand while singing the words from one through

five. When the number five is reached the left hand is closed. The singer reverses hands for the numbers from six through ten.

Tanzania: Right on Track

1. Using a world map find the country of Tanzania. What countries

is it near? Find out whether or not these countries are good neighbors for Tanzania to have.

2. Check out Tanzania's climate and crops. What do your findings indicate about the food, clothing, and shelter in Tanzania?

3. Go on a trek to the library. Find out how many people live in Tanzania. How long has it been an independent country? What problems does Tanzania face? While you are at it, you might look up the word "trek." What region of Africa is this word associated with? Hint: It has nothing to do with Tanzania!

Lee - mweh, ee - vee - ree, ee - tah - too, ee - neh, ee - tah - no, moo - tahn - dah - too, moo - foon - gah - tee, moo - nah - na, ee - ken - da, ee - koo - mee.

Rock On

The history of rock music is a lesson in the hopes, dreams, and fears of earthpeople. The story of rock is the story of the young and the young-at-heart. The melancholy blues, elaborate jazz, down-home country music, folk ballads, and the gospel spirit of soul music have all shaped the music we call rock.

Each rock song has a message, sometimes buried beneath the music and its pounding beat. The words and their repetitions, sometimes simple, sometimes not, unite with the music to carry the message. People of all nations, races, and religions listen to, play, and dance to rock music. The musical language of rock tunes us in to where we've been, where we are, and where we're going. Even modern 'disco'' music is rock music in disguise.

The following activities will help you reach "rock bottom" as you study the history of rock-and-roll.

History in the Years BR (Before Rock)

Some of the big music stars prior to the mid 1950s rock-and-roll explosion were Perry Como, Eddie Fisher, Kay Starr, and Joni James. All of them sang songs about love, songs with simple melodies and lyrics. The beat was not too important in this easy-listening music.

Prerock Record Research

1. Find some records that were cut during the 1950s by any of these people. Your parents or relatives might own copies. Listen to the music and the words. What is your opinion of the music?

2. Find someone who was a teenager in the early 1950s and get an opinion about any songs recorded by music stars of the BR years that this person remembers. Were many music stars from minority groups?

In the Beginning

Most people would agree that Bill Haley and the Comets was the first group of musicians to become rock stars. To find out about this group try the following activities.

The Comets' Meteoric Rise to Fame

1. Interview a person who was a teenager in the early 1950s. Jar this person's memory with the titles of the following hit songs: "Crazy Man, Crazy"; "Shake, Rattle and Roll"; "Rock Around the Clock"; "See You Later Alligator"; "Rockin' Through the Rye"; and "Saints' Rock and Roll."

2. Does the person remember the words or tunes to any of the songs?

3. If so, listen carefully to find out what the songs were about.

The One and Only ELVIS

Elvis Presley was the first individual star of rock music. In the mid 1950s everyone seemed to have heard of this singer. When you mentioned his first name people immediately knew whom you meant.

Delve into Elvis

1. Interview a "teenager" of the mid 1950s. Does this person remember any of the words or music to Elvis' hit songs? Elvis made his audiences tremble to the tunes of "Heartbreak Hotel"; "Blue Suede Shoes"; "I Want You, I Need You, I Love You"; "Don't Be Cruel"; "Hound Dog"; and "Love Me Tender."

2. Find some early Elvis Presley albums or records. Play them and listen to both the words and the music. Why did earthpeople like his music so much? Not everyone was wild about Elvis!

Rockin' and Rollin', Dancin' and Prancin'

Rock music is easy to dance to because its beat is so strong. Ask some people who were teenagers in the late fifties and early sixties to show you how people danced to rock-and-roll music. Ask them to do the Twist, Stroll, Locomotion, and Mashed Potatos. How did one "dress for dancing" back then?

English Rockers—The Beatles and Others

In the mid 1960s groups from England began to influence rock music all over the world. This activity focuses on five important early English rock groups. Use the following interview card to find out if any of today's teenagers has heard of these English groups. Then listen to some records and try to identify the distinctively English contribution to rock-and-roll.

	Have you ever heard of them?		Which of their songs do you remember?
Beatles	☐ yes	☐ no	
Rolling Stones	☐ yes	☐ no	
Gerry and the Pacemakers	☐ yes	☐ no	
Herman's Hermits	☐ yes	☐ no	
Dave Clark Five	☐ yes	☐ no	

Chuck Berry

Chuck Berry, one of the first black performers to become a rock-and-roll star, is an excellent guitar player as well as rock singer.

Check into Chuck

1. Go back to your sources of information—those teenagers of the late 1950s and early 1960s. If possible, get them to supply the words and music to the following Chuck Berry hits: "Maybellene," "School Days," "Sweet Little Sixteen," "Rock and Roll Music," "Johnny B. Goode," "Carol," and "Roll Over Beethoven."

2. Find out how Chuck Berry promoted himself as a rock singer.

Instrument History

Have you ever been to a live performance of an orchestra? If you have, you probably noticed that the musicians are seated in groups. Violinists are near each other, flutists are near each other, and so on. Look at the illustration to familiarize yourself with the names of the instruments and the organization of an orchestra.

Each of the instruments you hear in an orchestra of today has a history that goes back hundreds and even thousands of years. Why not be instrumental in tracking down the history of some of the instruments in a modern orchestra? Make a research card like the following to help you carry out your detective work. You'll also interview people who play the instruments you are researching, so keep them in mind as a source of information.

Name of instrument _____
What material is it made of?_____
Where and when was it first used? _____
What kind of sound does it produce?_____
(Think about whether it's a percussion, woodwind, or stringed instrument.)
Instrumentalist Interview Questions:
1. Is your instrument easy or hard to play? 2. How much do you practice? 3. What do you like best and least about your instrument? 4. Who do you think is the world's best player of the instrument?

Music to Your Ears: Sourcebooks

Amtann, Willy. *Music in Canada: 1600–1800*. Cambridge, Ontario: Habitex Books, 1975. Distributed by Collier-Macmillan Canada.

Belz, Carl. *The Story of Rock*. New York: Oxford University Press, 1972.

Eisen, Jonathan, ed. *Age of Rock*. New York: Random House, 1970.

Gabree, John. *The World of Rock*. Greenwich, Conn.: Fawcett Publications, 1960.

Glassie, Henry, et al. *Folksongs and Their Makers*. Bowling Green, Ohio: Bowling Green University Press, 1971.

Gleason, Ralph J. *The Jefferson Airplane and the San Francisco Sound*. New York: Ballantine Books, 1969.

Gold, Robert. *Jazz Talk: A Dictionary of Colorful Language That Has Emerged from America's Own Music*. Indianapolis: Bobbs-Merrill, 1975.

Harwell, Richard Barksdale. *Confederate Music*. Chapel Hill: University of North Carolina Press, 1950.

Hentoff, Nat, and McCarthy, Albert J., eds. *Jazz: New Perspectives on the History of Jazz by Twelve of the World's Foremost Critics and Scholars*. New York: DaCapo Press, 1975.

Lomax, Alan. *Folk Songs of North America*. Garden City, N.Y.: Doubleday, 1975.

Lydon, Michael. *Rock Folk*. New York: Dell Publishing, 1973.

Moogk, Edward B. *Roll Back the Years: History of Canadian Recorded Sound and Its Legacy, Genesis to 1930*. Ottawa: National Library of Canada, 1975.

Nketia, J. H. Kwabena. *African Music in Ghana*. Evanston, Ill.: Northwestern University Press, 1963.

———. *The Music of Africa*. New York: W. W. Norton, 1974.

Roberts, John S. *Black Music of Two Worlds*. New York: Praeger Publishers, 1972.

Robinson, Richard, and Zwerling, Andy. *The Rock Scene*. New York: Pyramid Books, 1971.

Silber, Irwin, ed. *Folksong Festival*. Englewood Cliffs, N.J.: School Book Service, 1969.

Standifer, James A., and Reeder, Barbara. *Source Book of African and Afro-American Materials for Music Educators*. Washington, D.C.: Contemporary Music Project, Music Educators National Conference, 1972.

Shaw, Arnold. *Rockin' Fifties: The Decade That Transformed the Pop Music Scene*. New York: Hawthorn Books, 1975.

Records From Near and Far

Here is a list of record companies that can bring earthmusic from the far corners of our planet—on a silver "platter," you might say! You can write to them for a listing of records, which you can order from any local record store or directly from the record company.

Record Companies

ABC, 8255 Beverly Blvd., Los Angeles, CA 90048

Audio Fidelity, 221 W. 57th St., New York, NY 10019

Capitol, 1750 N. Vine St., Hollywood, CA 90028

Columbia, 51 W. 52nd St., New York, NY 10019

Elektra, 15 Columbus Circle, New York, NY 10023

Everest, 10920 Wilshire Blvd. W., Los Angeles, CA 90024

Fiesta, 1690 Broadway, New York, NY 10019

Folkways, 43 W. 61st St., New York, NY 10023

London, 539 W. 25th St., New York, NY 10001

Lyrichord, 141 Perry St., New York, NY 10014

Nonesuch (Distributed by Elktra, listed above)

Philips, 35 E. Wacker Drive, Chicago, IL 60601

Request, 3800 S. Ocean Drive, Hollywood, FL 33019

Vanguard, 71 W. 23rd St., New York, NY 10010

Just for the Record

1. Listen to and enjoy some music from other lands. What would it be like to live in the countries that the music is from?

2. Find each country on a map. Is it near or far away from where you live? Does the music sound at all like music you are used to hearing?

3. Compare the music of two countries that are neighbors.

4. Compare the music of two countries that are far apart.

5. If the record jacket carries the music lyrics, try to sing some of the songs.

6. If you have a record whose lyrics aren't translated on the record jacket, try to translate them yourself.

7. Do you know of any new people in town that have recently moved there from a country whose music you have on record? Go visit them and ask them to listen to the record with you. Can they tell you about their music and their country?

15

Dollars and Sense

Do you remember when you could buy a 5¢ chocolate bar that was more than a nibble? Of course not—that was once upon a time for you. Once upon a time you could buy a vanilla shake of ice cream, milk, and flavor from vanilla beans, too.

Today the 5¢ chocolate bar may cost 26¢ and is so light that you have to eat it before it floats out of your hand. The vanilla shake probably has imitation vanilla flavoring and "real" 100% soybean oil! That's right—the *milk*shake made with milk products is a dying species. Perhaps someday parents will take their children to refrigerated museums where now-extinct real vanilla milkshakes are preserved under glass.

To survive in this changing world each earthperson needs to learn ways to get the best value out of every cent spent. We all seem to be spending more and more—and getting less and less. This chapter has activities to help you understand how TV commercials and magazine ads try to get you to buy things that you don't really want or need. You will also learn how to be a smart shopper and stretch your money.

We call this chapter "Dollars and Sense" in the hopes that it will bring about a *change* in your thinking. After all, there are two sides to every coin, and we wouldn't want you to take any wooden nickels now, would we?

The Tube

Television affects our lives, whether we watch it or not. Much that is spoken, written, or sung refers to television, so we experience TV in some form. Children, teenagers, and adults spend a great deal of time watching cartoon shows, sporting events, drama, movies, newscasts, and even soap operas, available at a push of the "on" button and a twirl of the dials.

A constant companion to these programs is the commercial. Each day hundreds of them tell us how to control dandruff, sweeten bad breath, and avoid ring around the collar. The following activity may astound you as you discover the number of TV commercials and the range of products they advertise. Find a watch or clock with a second hand, a pencil, and station yourself in front of a television set.

TV Survey

Select one channel to study. If other people want to do the study, have each person select a different channel. Do the first part of the survey on a Saturday morning. Do the other two parts on a weekday. Be sure to watch one *full* hour for each part of the survey.

Commercial Comparison

1. What age level and kind of people seem to be targets for the commercials at each of the time periods you studied?

2. Do you think that the people who watch the programs during each time slot are likely to be consumers of the products advertised?

3. Are you surprised by the number of commercials during each of the hour time periods?

4. Are you tempted to buy any of the products you saw advertised?

5. How do you feel (angry, sad, happy, bored, or other) about any of the advertising or programs that you saw?

	Saturday Morning (10:00-11:00)	Weekday Afternoon (4:00-5:00)	Weekday Evening (8:00-9:00)
Channel _____ List the shows you saw.			
How many commercials were there? List the subject of each commercial and how many seconds it ran.			
How many total seconds of commercials were there? Minutes? (Divide the seconds by 60.) How many commercials were public service messages (cancer society, for example)? How many commercials advertised each of the following products of services? (Add categories to this list.)			
Soft drinks			
Beer or wine			
Candy			
Food			
Toys			
Oil & gas companies			
Car parts (batteries, tires, and so on)			
Cameras			
Dishwashing or laundry soap			
Home appliances			
Garden or lawn tools or products			
_____			
_____			
_____			
_____			
Commercials for other programs			

The Saturday Morning Sale of the "Secret Ingredient"

Every Saturday morning young children watch television for hours. Every program sponsor presents commercials to convince children to buy or ask their parents to buy something. Many of the commercials are for toys. Many others are for "food" products. Yes, Saturday morning is munchies morning, and the commercials are the munchies morning mystery, for they advertise a secret ingredient! That's right, an ingredient so secret that it is seldom mentioned by name. This activity puts you on the path to finding out what is really being sold to children on Saturday mornings.

Watch an hour of Saturday morning television on each of two channels. Enter the names of the "food" products advertised during each hour on the following chart, then take your list to a local grocery store and find each product. On your chart, list the three major ingredients in each "food." The package label lists the ingredients in order of greatest to smallest proportions contained in the product.

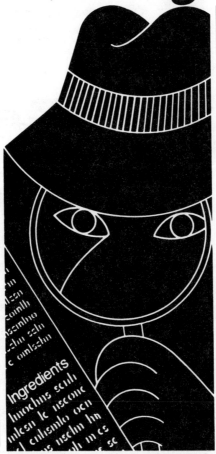

Don't get thrown off the track of the secret ingredient. Some products list one or more fancy names for the ingredient so that the buyer won't realize the real proportion of the secret ingredient in the product. Check any suspicious names for ingredients in a dictionary, for example, sucrose and lactose. Corn syrup is a major ingredient in some products. Find out what corn syrup is.

There Are No Secrets Here!

1. What is the secret ingredient?
2. How do you feel about its sale to children?
3. Do you think that most parents know about this Saturday morning sales pitch?
4. Did you ever bug your parents until they finally bought you some "food" product you saw advertised on TV?
5. Do you think that these commercials o_ fair and honest? If you don't think so, how could they be improved?

Channel		Date		Time	
Names of the food products					
Ingredients	1.		1.		1.
	2.		2.		2.
	3.		3.		3.

Channel		Date		Time	
Names of the food products					
Ingredients	1.		1.		1.
	2.		2.		2.
	3.		3.		3.

The Secret Seven

Advertisements in magazines or newspapers show us products that we may wish to buy. Wise consumers know that advertisers may try to get them to buy something that they don't really need. How do they do this? In this activity you'll learn about seven of their "winning" ways. You shouldn't get a product just because the ad gets to *you*. Here are the secrets of the seven, then.

1. Everyone has one: Join the crowd; everyone else has one, why don't you? Example: cola advertisements with happy, smiling, singing, *drinking* people.

2. Male-female attraction: If you use this, you'll be popular with the opposite sex. Example: after a girl has finished brushing her teeth with toothpaste, we see boys attracted to her because of her white teeth and wonderful breath.

3. Getting ahead: People who use this product are very successful; if you use this product, you'll be successful, too. Example: students who type their homework on portable typewriters get better grades than students who don't.

4. Something new: If you like things that are new and different, this product is for you. Example: "Crunchy Munch cereal has that brand-new peanut-butter-and-jelly flavor. Try it for a new kind of taste in the morning."

5. You are different: You are a special kind of person who is different from everyone else. Example: "Only special people should have the new Panther sports car—people who can tame it."

6. It's the *best*: This product does what it does better than any other product. Example: "Use Night Kill Cough Syrup. It will kill your cough better than any other cough syrup."

7. You deserve one: Pamper

yourself; you really deserve to have one of these. Example: "You deserve a break someday—eat at Snackdonald's."

Ad-ded Attractions

1. Get an old copy of a favorite magazine and cut out every ad. Now try to group each ad into one of the seven categories. Some ads may use more than one of the seven ways, so try to select the one that seems to be the most important. Hint: Look at any photograph or art work in the ad very carefully. The art or photos usually send the most important part of the product's message.

2. Write your own ad for each of the secret seven. Don't fall under the spell of your own ad!

A Helpful TV Commercial

As part of a small group, select a problem in your town or school that a 60 second TV commercial might alleviate. Then create the commercial by writing the script and planning what the camera will film. Video-tape the commercial to see its effect. Your school or local TV station may let you use its video tape equipment. Who knows—maybe you can even broadcast your commercial!

Public Service Commercial Cues
1. Town: Discouragement of the use of cigarettes, beer, wine, liquor, and drugs; cleanup of a stream, river, or park area; tactics for children to use if approached by strangers; fire prevention in the home.
2. School: discouragement of pushing and shoving in hallways; encouragement of attendance at an afterschool activity (sports, debates, etc.); advising against littering the school grounds; cafeteria manners.

Public Service Postthoughts
1. What problems did you have making the commercial?
2. Would the commercial appeal to TV viewers?
3. How could you improve the commercial?

TV Commercial Worksheet
A Public Service Message

What are the names of the people planning the commercial?

What problem or situation will the commercial try to improve?

Describe the commercial.
How will it start?

What will the "filling" (middle segment) be?

How will it end?

Write your script on another sheet of paper. For each part or scene, indicate duration (in seconds), video (what will the camera show?), dialogue, props, and music (if applicable).

Supermarket Savvy

You can become a clever consumer if you learn to shop in a supermarket so that you get the most food product for your money. Because foods are often packed in unusual quantities, it is difficult to determine which product is really cheapest. Unit pricing laws in many places now require supermarkets to show both the price for a packaged item and the price per unit of the item. Unit price is the item's cost per unit weight or volume. Unit prices are usually shown on a card right below the product on the shelf. The unit price label on the shelf reflects the cost per ounce, per pound, per gram, per quart, or per liter.

To benefit from unit price information, you must know how to use it. For this activity, write down on the chart on page 146 the names of three kinds of canned or packaged food that you like. Now, skip to a supermarket and find three brands of each food that are packaged in containers of the same approximate size. Find the unit price label on the shelf for each brand and write it down. Compare the unit prices for the three brands and place a check mark next to the best buy on your chart.

Kind of Food	Brand Names	Unit Price	Best Buy

Sizing Up the Situation
Some people always buy the largest size of a food product because they think that it's the best value. Pick out your favorite type of packaged food and list it below. Now go to a supermarket and select a brand of that food that comes in at least two different-sized packages. Compare the unit price of the large size with that of the smaller size. Which is the best buy? Compare unit prices on other foods to find out if biggest is always best.

Food

Unit Price for Large Size

Unit Price for Small Size

Best Buy

Snooper Marketing

Most communities have one or more Grand Onions, Win Pixies, Atlantic and Specifics, or Shopbright markets. Have you ever shopped in one? That buzz coming through the background music is not static but the sound of shoppers thinking, "How can I save money? Which is the best buy?"

The smart consumer is an earth-person who goes snooping before shopping to find out which markets have the lowest prices on different foods. Here is an activity that may save you and your family a good deal of money. All you need are a pencil, a shopping list, and boundless energy. You can compare supermarkets or supermarkets and small grocery stores. You may even

want to find out if prices in supermarkets and small grocery stores are the same in poor and rich neighborhoods. You may be in for some big surprises as you snoop around.

Make up a shopping list to use in each store you visit. Include canned and frozen foods; produce; grain, dairy, and meat products; and some nonfood products on your list. Find the lowest-priced item to fit the description on the list, always comparing the same weights or volumes. Don't be surprised if the cheapest item is not always a name brand. Do all your comparison shopping (snooping) in the same week because food prices can change rapidly.

Store-ing Up Information

1. Which store had the lowest total price for all the items?

2. Go through your list and put a check mark next to the lowest price for each item. Now look at the list to find out which store had the lowest prices on each kind of item.

3. Did any of the stores have special gimmicks, such as trading stamps or supermarket bingo, to get people to shop there?

4. Were some stores cleaner than others? What else did you notice about each store (width of aisles, freshness of produce, for example)?

5. If you compared stores in different neighborhoods, what did you discover about their prices?

Catalog Shopping

Some people like to shop by mail to save both time and money. Various companies do a large mail order business and send out millions of catalogs each year. Three large North American companies that ship their catalog items around the world are J. C. Penney Co., Montgomery Ward, and Sears, Roebuck & Co.

In the following activity you'll compare items that appear in mail order catalogs for money value. First, get hold of a recent catalog from each of two mail order companies. You may be able to borrow them from friends and relatives. If a mail order company has a catalog showroom in your town you'll be able to use the store's copy of the catalog for the activity.

Make a list of five items that you would like to buy, such as an article of clothing, musical instrument, or appliance. Find each item in two different catalogs. Read each advertisement carefully to be sure that the item offered by each company has the same features, materials, and so on. Note that the companies use their own brand name. For each item list the price and the shipping charge for home delivery. Total the two costs.

Order Your Thoughts
1. Which mail order company—if any—gives the best price on each item?
2. What are the advantages and disadvantages of catalog shopping?
3. What else should you consider besides price when you catalog shop?
4. Compare the catalog price of some of the items to their price in a local store.

Pollution and Conservation Gr Help! Food and Dru Consumer Rights Cons

Here are the addresses, and in some cases telephone numbers, of private and governmental groups who are interested in consumer rights. Each of them donates time and money to make things a little better for everyone. You can write to these groups for free descriptive newsletters or brochures. You might share this list of addresses with a local librarian and encourage him or her to subscribe to informative newsletters or magazines. Perhaps a guest speaker from one of these groups would come to your school, library, or community group.

Consumer Rights
Each of these groups or agencies has a special interest in protecting the consumer.

Name and Address	Some Interests
Bureau of Consumer Protection Federal Trade Commission Washington, DC 20580	Illegal/deceptive sales tactics; consumer fraud
Center for the Study of Responsive Law P.O. Box 19367 Washington, DC 20036	Consumer and personal rights laws
Citizen Action Group 133 C St., S.E. Washington, DC 20003	Organization of local and state consumer groups
Common Cause 2030 M St., N.W. Washington, DC 20036	Lobbying of Congress and the president to improve government
Congress Watch 133 C St., S.E. Washington, DC 20003	Keeping track of the voting records of senators and representatives
Consumer Federation of America Suite 406 1012 14th St., N.W. Washington, DC 20005 Tel.: (202) 737-3732	Organization of local and state consumer groups
Consumers Union 265 Washington St. Mt. Vernon, NY 10550 (914) 664-6400	Product testing and publication of results
Council of Better Business Bureaus 1150 17th St., N.W. Washington, DC 20036	Groups of businessmen who "police" their own products and services
Office of Consumer Affairs Washington, DC 20201 Consumer complaints: (202) 245-6093 State and local programs: (202) 245-9890	Consumer problems, laws, and education

Public Citizen Litigation Unit
7th Floor
2000 P St., N.W.
Washington, DC 20036

Lawsuits on public behalf
against companies and agencies

Pollution and Conservation Groups
These groups are interested in preserving the natural environment. Each publishes a magazine or newsletter.

Name and Address	Publication
Environmental Action, Inc. 1346 Connecticut Ave., N.W. Washington, DC 20036	*Environmental Action*
Friends of the Earth 529 Commercial St. San Francisco, CA 94111	*Not Man Apart*
National Audubon Society 950 Third Ave. New York, NY 10022	*Audubon*
National Wildlife Federation 1412 16th St., N.W. Washington, DC 20036	*National Wildlife;* *International Wildlife*
Sierra Club 1050 Mills Tower San Francisco, CA 94104	*Sierra Club Bulletin*
Wilderness Society 1901 Pennsylvania Ave., N.W. Washington, DC 20006	*Living Wilderness*

Food and Drugs
The Food and Drug Administration is interested in guarding against harmfulness in our foods, medicines, and cosmetics.

National Office
Consumer Product Safety Commission
Washington, DC 20207

Regional Offices
Consumer Product Safety Commission (for all addresses)
1330 W. Peachtree St., N.W., Atlanta, GA 30309, (404) 526-2231
408 Atlantic Ave., Boston, MA 02110, (617) 223-5576
5th Floor, 1 N. Wacker Dr., Chicago, IL 60606, (312) 353-8260
Room 1905, 911 Walnut St., Kansas City, MO 64106, (816) 374-2034
Suite 1100, 3660 Wilshire Blvd., Los Angeles, CA 90010, (213) 688-7272
Room 650, Federal Building, Fort Snelling, Twin Cities, MN 55111,
    (612) 725-3424
International Trade Mart, Suite 414, 2 Canal St., New Orleans, LA 70013,
    (504) 527-2102
Building 1, 8th Floor, Bay 7, 830 Third Ave., Brooklyn, NY 11232,
    (212) 788-5000, ext. 1166
Room 410-C, 500 S. Ervay, P.O. Box 15035, Dallas, TX 75201,
    (214) 749-3871
Suite 938, Guaranty Bank Building, 817-17th St., Denver, CO 80202,
    (303) 837-2904
10th Floor, Continental Building, 400 Market St., Philadelphia, PA 19106,
    (215) 597-9105
Room 558, 50 Fulton St., San Francisco, CA 94102, (415) 556-1816
1131 Federal Building, 909 First Ave., Seattle, WA 98104, (206) 442-5276
DEB Annex 21046, Brookpark Rd., Cleveland, OH 44135, (216) 522-3886

Dollars and Sense Sourcebooks: A Run for Your Money

Bloomstein, Morris J. *Consumer's Guide to Fighting Back.* New York: Dodd, Mead, 1976.

Brown, Les. *Television: The Business Behind the Box.* New York: Harcourt Brace Jovanovich, 1971.

Chisari, Francis V., and Nakamura, Robert M. *The Consumer's Guide to Health Care.* Boston: Little, Brown, 1976.

Goulart, Ron. *The Assault on Childhood.* Los Angeles: Sherbourne Press, 1969.

Magnuson, Warren G., and Carper, Jean. *The Dark Side of the Market Place: The Plight of the American Consumer.* Englewood Cliffs, N.J.: Prentice-Hall, 1965.

Melody, William. *Children's Television: The Economics of Exploitation.* New Haven: Yale University Press, 1973.

Stevens, Paul. *I Can Sell You Anything: How I Made Your Favorite TV Commercial With Minimum Truth and Maximum Consequences.* New York: P. A. Wyden, 1972.

Stuart, Frederic, ed. *Consumer Protection From Deceptive Advertising.* Hempstead, N.Y.: Hofstra University Press, 1974.

Thomas, Sarah M., and Weddington, Bernadine. *A Guide to Sources of Consumer Education.* Washington, D.C.: Information Resources Press, 1973.

Wasserman, Paul, ed. *Consumer Sourcebook.* Detroit: Gale Research, 1974.

Wight, Robin. *The Day The Pigs Refused to Be Driven to Market.* New York: Random House, 1974.

Winick, Charles. *Children's Television Commercials.* New York: Praeger Publishing, 1973.

16

Clear Skies Ahead?

(A Down-to-Earth Look Into the Future)

Predicting the future is nearly impossible. Human attitudes and values, discoveries and inventions, and natural disasters bring sudden and unforeseen changes. Thinking about the future is important, however, and neglecting the future could be disastrous to future generations.

We earthpeople must consider the effects of our actions on population, economic growth, energy, food, raw materials, pollution, space exploration, thermonuclear war, education, health, and applied science—to name just a few! Explore the future with us in this chapter. You'll find out what others have thought and are thinking, which will start you thinking, we think.

Are We Alone?

Do earthpeople have cosmic neighbors?

The Pioneer spacecraft, launched by NASA in 1972, was the first object that humans sent out of the solar system. In the event that the spacecraft would be found by extraterrestial life, it bore a message-carrying plaque on its outside. The plaque tells, through drawings, where the spacecraft has come from in the solar system and what we know about science. Most important, it shows an earthman and earthwoman. And they are greeting a yet-unknown intelligent being.

Of all the questions that earthpeople ask about space, we are most fascinated by the question of the existence of life elsewhere in the universe. Ask us another one—no one has yet come up with a definitive answer! We have good odds, however, on a "yes." The universe contains 10 billion galaxies, and there are about 100 billion stars in each galaxy. So, there are more than 100,000,000,000,000,000,000,000

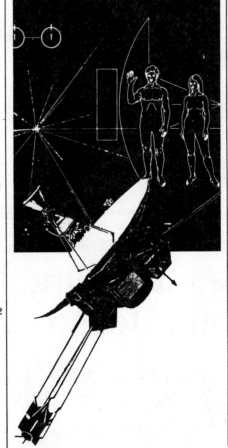

stars. Scientists think that most stars have satellites. The probability of existing earthlike planets is most likely not zero. Even these large numbers do not tell us what percentage of stars may contain planets with life. When we look skyward on a clear night our thoughts "revolve" as we wonder if we are alone.

To Start You Thinking

1. What effect would making contact with intelligent life elsewhere in the universe have on earthpeople?

2. Some people believe that if extraterrestial life contacted us first they would be more advanced than we and would probably know how to avoid a nuclear war. Write a fantasy story about what such an advanced society could teach us. What values and beliefs would these extraterrestrials hold?

3. How do you think most earthpeople regard projects for sending signals to communicate with life elsewhere in the universe? What is your attitude?

The New Biology—Decisions for the Future

Here are some possible newspaper headlines that you might read in the next 50 years. Read each of them and as part of a group choose one for your own newspaper article. Do some research to lay the scientific foundation for your story and let your imagination build the rest.

Distribute your story to the others in your group and collect theirs in return. Then write a "Letter to the Editor" about one or more of the stories.

Baby Born in Test Tube

There have been a good number of reports ... ... years or m... the mortali-
ty rate ...

CLONING — THE FIRST HUMAN BEING IS A SUCCESS

It's a first baby for 'he ... ing the ... in mid-May. If
K... 'e fi... ... it' ... ... be Lo...

HUMAN LIFE SPAN NOW APPROACHES 85 YEARS

By DONA C. BADER
Editor, The Union

Good morning! You have just stepped up in the world ...
...aled new heights. Climbed another rung on life's lad...
It's

New Law Requires Sterilization Of All Citizen With Genetic Defects Long Criminal Record and I.Q.'s Below 70

New York Times News Service

WASHINGTON — The Supreme Court yesterday r... that a state ... who approved the sterilization of a ... ...om her su...

FIRST BURN PATIENTS TREATED IN ORBITING SATELLITE HOSPITAL

Little Robert Santaguini lies in the Universe Hospital burn center re-cuper... ... last week's fiery ... ...

hospital and later transferred ... Universe Hospital where he is ... father

Against Genetic Surgery Society Pickets White House Demanding Changes In New Genetic Law

A decision by a handful of legislators this week is likely to ... tive plans that are bound to af-fect the ... ...illions ... ... hope the lawmakers have sifted ... ... fact and fiction in t'

Time Machine . . . Into the Future

A favorite science fiction story is *The Time Machine* by H. G. Wells, in which a man builds a machine that will carry him forward and backward in time.

Time travel has always been an absorbing (and timely!) subject. The fascination of the future usually prevails over that of the past. In this activity you are going to use your imagination to go forward 500 years in time.

Decide what you or your group will bring along to share with the future generation of earthpeople. Use the baggage chart to guide your work. The baggage compartment of your time machine will hold only one item from each category, so pack with care and prepare for

takeoff. . . .

. . . Five hundred years later, future earthpeople exclaim over your "artifacts." They have the

same general categories, but how different the specific items are! List and describe what they show you in the second column.

Time Machine Baggage

Category	Present Item	Its Future Form
Human being (outside the group)		
Book		
Law or code		
Word to the wise		
Movie		
Record		
Food		
Religious text		
Clothing		
Invention		
Work of art		
Technological product		
Governmental document		

"The Future Is Only a Forecast Away," We Predict

What will life feature in the future? Will most people be employed in white-collar or blue-collar jobs? Will the size of families increase or decrease? Will we run out of raw materials such as oil and coal? These are not easy questions to answer.

We use the terms "prediction" and "forecast" freely throughout this chapter. Prediction is based on already known facts or scientific calculations and often refers to specific events. A forecast of the future is more an estimation of trends and probabilities—an educated guess. The forecaster must think in terms of ifs, ands, or buts. Often several views of the future emerge, based on the maybes.

This activity will direct you to the information you need to predict and forecast the future. You will be searching out an area of interest, and we suggest that you work with a small group of people, each of you selecting one of the areas from the chart and working to fill in the columns under the headings. You will then have a varied forecast for the future. Well, how does it look for us earthpeople?

Looking Into the Future

Area for Study	Present Trends	New and Old Ideas	Famous People	Forecast for the Future (One or more—twenty-five words or less?)
Cities				
Communication				
Education				
Environment				
Family LIfe Styles				
Food and Crops				
Health and Care				
Housing				
Income				
Inventions				
Marriage				
Power and Energy				
Quality of Life				
Resources				
Transportation				
Work				

sce·nar·i·os (si ner′ ē ō, -när-) **n.,**
pl. **-i·os** [It., <L. *scaenarium*
<scaena, stage, SCENE]
An outline of the plot of a
dramatic work, indicating its
scenes, characters, and situations.

Scenarios of the Future

There are a number of modern scientists who use the processes of science to study and forecast the future. Most of them have used the year 2000 as a date to point toward. If you look upon their results as scenarios—outlines and descriptions of what the world might be like in the next 50 years—you can then try to fill in the details yourself. We have gathered the opinions of several well-known scientists. This is an opportunity for some research teamwork. Each team studies the reports of one scientist, reports back, and sets up a mock conference on the future (call it "To Be Continued"?). Charts, diagrams, pictures, reports, tapes, and other media will make reporting more interesting and informative.

Scientific Scenarios

Scientist*	Scenario
Daniel Bell (professor of sociology at Harvard)	Transportation will "shrink" the world. The environment will be safe but problems will still be in the air. More people will be working in service areas than in production of goods. People will be living in a more fragile and hostile world.
James Bonner (professor of biology at California Institute of Technology)	People will become either permanently poor or permanently rich. The advances of science will make it possible for human organs to heal themselves. If population in developing countries isn't checked, great famines will occur. Humans will find ways to preserve the brain, decode its messages, and produce a superspecies by cloning.
Arthur C. Clarke (inventor of communications satellite and writer of science fiction)	The wheel will give way to vehicles that float. Satellites will bring education and technology to underdeveloped nations and will promote colonization of space. Humans will set up cities on the moon. Our food source will be the protein in oil. Communication with the dead, levitation, robots, death rays, invisibility, and artificial life will be realities for us.
Margaret Mead (anthropologist and curator emeritus of the American Museum of Natural History)	Humans must find ways to deal with air- and water-pollution problems. Our culture will separate into age groups: The young and old will learn from their peers. Youth will take for granted satellites, war, computers, pollution, and population control and not seek for knowledge or commitment. They must participate directly in experiences and ask questions that they themselves answer. Education is the way to bring the generations together.

*Other scientists who have written and spoken on the future: Paul Ehrlich, Orville Freeman, Herman Kahn, John McHale, Jean Rostand, Alvin Toffler.

Appendix

Prevailing Winds

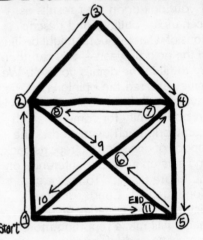

A Little Detective Work: Checkup

A. Snow Shovel

B. Bow Drill

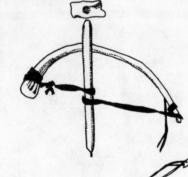

C. Drying Rack

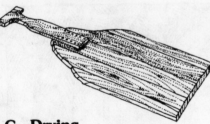

D. Harpoon

E. Cooking Pot

F. Needle and Sinew

Brain Teasers

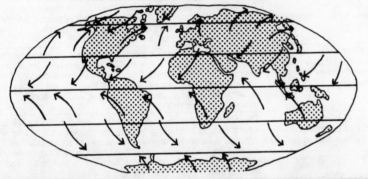

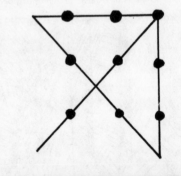

The Mysterious Continent

A. *Humid continental.*
B. *Mediterranean.*
C. *Desert.*
D. *Marine west coast.*
E. *Humid subtropical.*
F. *Steppe.*

Building an Igloo Game: Checkup

1

2

3

4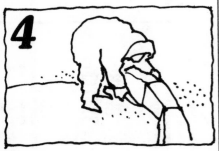

5

6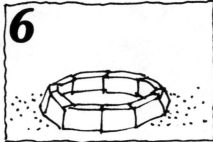

7

8

9

10

11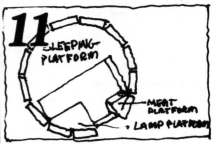

SLEEPING PLATFORM

MEAT PLATFORM

LAMP PLATFORM

12

13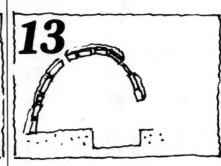

14

15

DISASTER GAME

VOLCANIC ROCK SYSTEM
DISASTER: Volcanic Eruption Respond with: Evacuation
200 Earth Balance Points needed to win

STORM SYSTEM
DISASTER: Lightning Respond with: Lightning Rod
200 Earth Balance Points needed to win

GRAVITY
DISASTER: Rock Slides Respond with: Zoning Laws
200 Earth Balance Points needed to win

WIND SYSTEM
DISASTER: Tornado Respond with: Tornado Alert
200 Earth Balance Points needed to win

RIVER SYSTEM
DISASTER: Flood or Cave-in Respond with: Conservation
200 Earth Balance Points needed to win

TECTONIC SYSTEM
DISASTER: Earthquake Respond with: Building Codes
200 Earth Balance Points needed to win

TECTONIC SYSTEM
DISASTER: Earthquake Respond with: Building Codes
200 Earth Balance Points needed to win

RIVER SYSTEM
DISASTER: Flood or Cave-in Respond with: Conservation
200 Earth Balance Points needed to win

WIND SYSTEM
DISASTER: Tornado Respond with: Tornado Alert
200 Earth Balance Points needed to win

GRAVITY
DISASTER: Rock Slides Respond with: Zoning Laws
200 Earth Balance Points needed to win

STORM SYSTEM
DISASTER: Lightning Respond with: Lightning Rod
200 Earth Balance Points needed to win

VOLCANIC ROCK SYSTEM
DISASTER: Volcanic Eruption Respond with: Evacuation
200 Earth Balance Points needed to win

How to Play

Objective: To get each system on your disaster board in balance by placing exactly 200 earth balance points in each space.

Materials: One set of *Disaster* cards, 1 disaster gameboard (each player to use half).

Number of Players: Two.

Game Rules: One player deals the *Disaster* cards, one at a time, until each player has seven cards. The dealer puts the next card face up between the players to form a discard pile.

The other player starts by picking a card from the top of the face-down stack or from the top of the discard pile. After drawing one card, the player can then do one of the following:

1. Place a **Disaster** card on any earth system on the opponent's gameboard, draw another card, and then discard one card. **cont.**

Rock Slide
Wet earth, soil, and rocks slide down a hillside, destroying vegetation and buildings.
Place over a *Gravity* card to stop.
Respond with a *Zoning Law* card to continue.

Rock Slide
Wet earth, soil, and rocks slide down a hillside, destroying vegetation and buildings.
Place over a *Gravity* card to stop.
Respond with a *Zoning Law* card to continue.

Rock Slide
Wet earth, soil, and rocks slide down a hillside, destroying vegetation and buildings.
Place over a *Gravity* card to stop.
Respond with a *Zoning Law* card to continue.

Lightning
Severe thunderstorm hits home. Potential fire and electrical damage.
Place over *Storm System* card to stop.
Respond with a *Lightning Rod* card to continue.

Lightning
Severe thunderstorm hits home. Potential fire and electrical damage.
Place over *Storm System* card to stop.
Respond with a *Lightning Rod* card to continue.

Lightning
Severe thunderstorm hits home. Potential fire and electrical damage.
Place over *Storm System* card to stop.
Respond with a *Lightning Rod* card to continue.

Evacuation
This is the best response if a volcano erupts. This action will keep you alive!
Place over a *Volcano* card before continuing.

Evacuation
This is the best response if a volcano erupts. This action will keep you alive!
Place over a *Volcano* card before continuing.

Evacuation
This is the best response if a volcano erupts. This action will keep you alive!
Place over a *Volcano* card before continuing.

Tornado Alert
Open windows, go to center of building, and take cover. This card will protect you and tell you what to do in case of a tornado.
Place over a *Tornado* card before continuing.

Tornado Alert
Open windows, go to center of building, and take cover. This card will protect you and tell you what to do in case of a tornado.
Place over a *Tornado* card before continuing.

Tornado Alert
Open windows, go to center of building, and take cover. This card will protect you and tell you what to do in case of a tornado.
Place over a *Tornado* card before continuing.

Volcano
A volcano has erupted, spilling hot lava on the earth's surface.
Place above a *Volcanic Rock System* card to stop.
Respond with an *Evacuation* card to continue.

Volcano
A volcano has erupted, spilling hot lava on the earth's surface.
Place above a *Volcanic Rock System* card to stop.
Respond with an *Evacuation* card to continue.

Volcano
A volcano has erupted, spilling hot lava on the earth's surface.
Place above a *Volcanic Rock System* card to stop.
Respond with an *Evacuation* card to continue.

Flood
A river has flooded beyond its flood plain. Erosion increases; buildings and homes are destroyed.
Place above a *River System* card to stop.
Respond with a *Conservation* card to continue.

Flood
A river has flooded beyond its flood plain. Erosion increases; buildings and homes are destroyed.
Place above a *River System* card to stop.
Respond with a *Conservation* card to continue.

Flood
A river has flooded beyond its flood plain. Erosion increases; buildings and homes are destroyed.
Place above a *River System* card to stop.
Respond with a *Conservation* card to continue.

Tornado
A tornado has been sighted and reported by the weather bureau.
Place over a *Wind System* card to stop.
Respond with a *Tornado Alert* card to continue.

Tornado
A tornado has been sighted and reported by the weather bureau.
Place over a *Wind System* card to stop.
Respond with a *Tornado Alert* card to continue.

Tornado
A tornado has been sighted and reported by the weather bureau.
Place over a *Wind System* card to stop.
Respond with a *Tornado Alert* card to continue.

Earthquake
The earth begins to shake and roll; buildings begin to collapse.
Place over a *Tectonic System* card to stop.
Respond with a *Building Codes* card to continue.

Earthquake
The earth begins to shake and roll; buildings begin to collapse.
Place over a *Tectonic System* card to stop.
Respond with a *Building Codes* card to continue.

Earthquake
The earth begins to shake and roll; buildings begin to collapse.
Place over a *Tectonic System* card to stop.
Respond with a *Building Codes* card to continue.

Conservation
Conservation techniques such as terracing, building higher levees, and revegetation can help control erosion by flooding.
Place over a *Flood* card before continuing.

Conservation
Conservation techniques such as terracing, building higher levees, and revegetation can help control erosion by flooding.
Place over a *Flood* card before continuing.

Conservation
Conservation techniques such as terracing, building higher levees, and revegetation can help control erosion by flooding.
Place over a *Flood* card before continuing.

Zoning Laws
Better zoning laws would prohibit construction in areas of weak rocks.
Place over a *Rock Slide* card before continuing.

Zoning Laws
Better zoning laws would prohibit construction in areas of weak rocks.
Place over a *Rock Slide* card before continuing.

Zoning Laws
Better zoning laws would prohibit construction in areas of weak rocks.
Place over a *Rock Slide* card before continuing.

DISASTER GAME	DISASTER GAME	DISASTER GAME	DISASTER GAME	2. *Place an* Earth Balance Points *card on any of his or her earth systems, draw as many cards as were placed on the gameboard, and then discard one card.* 3. *Discard one card.* A player who has a disaster occurring in any system cannot continue play until the correct *Response* card is placed on top of the disaster. The only move open to this player is to draw and discard cards. Exactly 200 earth balance points secure a system from disaster. Any value on the system less than 200 does not. If a *Disaster* card is placed on a system that has less than 200 points, the player loses whatever earth balance points are on that system. *End of Game:* Play ends when one player has exactly 200 earth balance points for each system on his or her gameboard.
DISASTER GAME	DISASTER GAME	DISASTER GAME	DISASTER GAME	
DISASTER GAME	DISASTER GAME	DISASTER GAME	DISASTER GAME	
DISASTER GAME	DISASTER GAME	DISASTER GAME	DISASTER GAME	DISASTER GAME
DISASTER GAME	DISASTER GAME	DISASTER GAME	DISASTER GAME	DISASTER GAME
DISASTER GAME	DISASTER GAME	DISASTER GAME	DISASTER GAME	DISASTER GAME

Lightning Rod This card will ground you and the structure you are in. It will save your life. Place over a *Lightning* card before continuing.	**50** Earth Balance Points	**50** Earth Balance Points	**100** Earth Balance Points	**100** Earth Balance Points	**100** Earth Balance Points
Lightning Rod This card will ground you and the structure you are in. It will save your life. Place over a *Lightning* card before continuing.	**50** Earth Balance Points	**50** Earth Balance Points	**100** Earth Balance Points	**100** Earth Balance Points	**150** Earth Balance Points
Lightning Rod This card will ground you and the structure you are in. It will save your life. Place over a *Lightning* card before continuing.	**50** Earth Balance Points	**50** Earth Balance Points	**100** Earth Balance Points	**100** Earth Balance Points	**150** Earth Balance Points
Building Codes Designing and locating buildings to withstand earthquakes is possible. This card will do it. Place over an *Earthquake* card before continuing.	**50** Earth Balance Points	**50** Earth Balance Points	**100** Earth Balance Points	**100** Earth Balance Points	**150** Earth Balance Points
Building Codes Designing and locating buildings to withstand earthquakes is possible. This card will do it. Place over an *Earthquake* card before continuing.	**50** Earth Balance Points	**100** Earth Balance Points	**100** Earth Balance Points	**100** Earth Balance Points	**150** Earth Balance Points
Building Codes Designing and locating buildings to withstand earthquakes is possible. This card will do it. Place over an *Earthquake* card before continuing.	**50** Earth Balance Points	**100** Earth Balance Points	**100** Earth Balance Points	**100** Earth Balance Points	**150** Earth Balance Points

DISASTER GAME	DISASTER GAME	DISASTER GAME	DISASTER GAME	DISASTER GAME	DISASTER GAME
DISASTER GAME	DISASTER GAME	DISASTER GAME	DISASTER GAME	DISASTER GAME	DISASTER GAME
DISASTER GAME	DISASTER GAME	DISASTER GAME	DISASTER GAME	DISASTER GAME	DISASTER GAME
DISASTER GAME	DISASTER GAME	DISASTER GAME	DISASTER GAME	DISASTER GAME	DISASTER GAME
DISASTER GAME	DISASTER GAME	DISASTER GAME	DISASTER GAME	DISASTER GAME	DISASTER GAME

The Real Thing Game
Low Risk Cards

What is the most boring thing that ever happened to you?

Make sounds to match the following actions (do each):
a. moaning
b. whistling
c. crying

Tell a silly joke.

Tell the group how you feel about playing this game, but do not use words.

List two things that you think should be taught in school that are not being taught now.

Tell the group something good that happened to you this week.

What would you do if someone gave you $50, no strings attached?

What would you do if a person accidentally punched you hard?

Give a 2 minute speech on "How I Think My School Should Be Changed."

List at least three things you would like to have adults do that they are not doing now.

Describe something you have done that made someone else feel good.

Act out any one of the following so that the other players guess it. Don't use words or props and do not read aloud below this line.
a. ping-pong game b. your favorite TV show

List at least three things you would like to have kids do that they are not doing now.

Tell the group how you feel about sports in your school.

Describe one thing that other people have told you that you do well.

Tell the group something bad that happened to you this year.

What was your favorite teacher like?

Tell the group two things that make you angry.

Shake hands with each person in the group.

What do you think happens when someone dies?

Name a book that you have read in the last month and try to convince the others to read it.

Wink at each person in the group.

Sing a song.

Low Risk Card	Low Risk Card	
Low Risk Card	Low Risk Card	Low Risk Card
Low Risk Card	Low Risk Card	Low Risk Card
Low Risk Card	Low Risk Card	Low Risk Card
Low Risk Card	Low Risk Card	Low Risk Card
Low Risk Card	Low Risk Card	Low Risk Card
Low Risk Card	Low Risk Card	Low Risk Card
Low Risk Card	Low Risk Card	Low Risk Card

The Real Thing Game **High Risk Cards**	*Tell the group something about yourself that no one else knows.*	*Walk the way people do when they are feeling as follows (do each):* *a. mad* *b. happy* *c. sad* *d. stubborn*
Give each person a hug.	*Act out without words something you would like to improve about yourself.*	*Walk like one of the members in this group.*
Tell the group at least three of your strengths.	*Do whatever you would like to do with each member of the group.*	*Tell the group one thing you like and dislike about the opposite sex.*
Tell the group how you felt when someone you loved died.	*Do a 1 minute dance.*	*Describe your greatest achievement to date in your life.*
Tell each person something positive about that person.	*Without words, express a strong feeling to one member of the group.*	*Answer the question, Who Am I? ten times.*
Describe the most painful experience you ever had.	*Look one person in the eyes for 1 minute.*	*How do you feel about dating?*
What do your parents think about your dating other people?	*Tell the group whether or not you believe in God.*	*Tell how you feel about your body.*
Make up an advertisement about yourself and describe it to the group.	*Give the name of the person you love the most and why you do.*	*Without words, show each person individually how you feel about him or her.*

High Risk Card	**High Risk Card**	
High Risk Card	**High Risk Card**	**High Risk Card**
High Risk Card	**High Risk Card**	**High Risk Card**
High Risk Card	**High Risk Card**	**High Risk Card**
High Risk Card	**High Risk Card**	**High Risk Card**
High Risk Card	**High Risk Card**	**High Risk Card**
High Risk Card	**High Risk Card**	**High Risk Card**
High Risk Card	**High Risk Card**	**High Risk Card**

The Real Thing

For rules to the
Real Thing Game,
see page 20.

Index

A
Adams, John Quincy, 46–47
advertising, 141–144
African crafts, 102, 103
Anthony, Susan B., 58
anthropology, 2–11, 35–41
archaeology, 4
Australopithecus, 2

B
baboons, 9–11
Beatles, 137
Bell, Daniel, 155
Berry, Chuck, 137
big bang theory, 1–2
birth, 14
Bonner, James, 155
brain hemispheres, 26

C
cave art, 6
cemeteries, 72–73
Chavez. Cesar, 59–60
Chief Joseph, 59
Children's Bill of Rights, 52
chimpanzee sign language, 38
Chisholm, Shirley, 61
Clarke, Arthur C., 155
climate, 80–81
codes, 40–41
consumer rights, 148–149
consumerism, 141–149
contour map, 90
crafts, 5, 101–109

D
da Vinci, Leonardo, 44
Daruma dolls, 106
dashiki, 101
democracy, 43
Disaster Game, 77
dowsers, 96

E
earth, measurement of, 77–78
embryos, 13
Eratosthenes, 77–78
Eskimo tools, 39
Estes Park, 88–90

F
Fong, Hiram, 60
food, 111–121
food buying, 145–146, 147
Friedan, Betty, 62
freedom time line, 49
Freud, Sigmund, 17
futurism, 151–155

G
geography, 83
geology, 83
Goodall, Jane, 8
Greek city-state, 43
guinea pigs, 28–29

H
Haley, Bill, 136
heredity, 20–21
history, 43–63
Homo erectus, 2–3
Homo sapiens, 3

I
igloo building, 36
Igloo Game, 37
instruments, musical, 138

JK
King, Martin Luther, Jr., 48–49
Köppen, Wladimir, 79

L
language, 38–41
learning, 23–25
life cycles, 15
Lincoln, Abraham, 45

M
mail order catalogs, 68–71, 148
mapping games, 86–87
Maslow, Abraham, 17
maze learning, 28, 30, 31
Mead, Margaret, 35–36, 155
mealworms, 30–31
meditation, 25–26
Meredith, James, 53
mirbadakan, 128
Mott, Lucretia, 47–48
music, 131–139

N
Nairobi Game Park, 9–11
national parks, 84–85
nuclear power, 95

O
ocean currents, 81
optical illusions, 32–33

P
Pankhurst, Emmeline, 57
Pavlov, Ivan, 27
Pei, Ieoh Ming, 61
Piaget, Jean, 27
piñata, 107
Presley, Elvis, 136
psychology, 13–21, 23–33
pysanka egg, 109

QR
Real Thing game, 20–21
records, phonograph, 139
Renaissance, 44
resources, 93–99
rock music, 136–137
Rogers, Carl, 16

S
self-image, 18–19
Shumacher, E. F., 99
sign language, 38–39
sports and games, 123–129
stamp collecting, 123–125
Steinem, Gloria, 63

T
technology, soft and hard, 98–99
television, 141–143
thinking games, 24–25
Tijerina, Reies Lopes, 62
time capsule, 6
tombstones, 72–73
Turner, Nat, 56

UV
vinta, 108

W
Waldrop, Anne, 50–51
Watson, John B., 17
Wheatley, Phyllis, 54
women's rights, 50–51, 57–58, 62, 63
woodmongers, 94

XYZ
zabott, 129

From The Earthpeople Activity Book, Copyright © 1978 by Abruscato & Hassard and Goodyear Publishing Co., Inc.